BOTALLACK

Cyril Noall

DYLLANSOW TRURAN

"Botallack has been called a royal mine, but although we may not perhaps aspire to royalty, we hope soon to take a respectable position among the aristocracy."

Captain James Roach, addressing Botallack adventurers on February 15th, 1882.

First published in 1972
Bradford Barton

This edition published 1999

Dyllansow Truran
Croft Prince, Mount Hawke, Truro, Cornwall TR4 8EE

ISBN 1 85022 120 0 (cased)

ISBN 1 85022 121 9 (paperback)

PRINTED AND BOUND IN CORNWALL BY
R. Booth (Bookbinder) Ltd. & Troutbeck Press
Antron Hill, Mabe, Penryn TR10 9HH

Main text set in 10/12 Times Roman

Contents

The publishers gratefully acknowledge the generosity of Mrs W. L. Sevier in allowing them to use photographs from her collection. No 9,10,11 and 14 - 23 inclusive taken by J. C. Burrow and others.

Photographs 1- 8 inclusive and 24 are reproduced by permission of The Royal Institute of Cornwall.

The publishers acknowledge the assistance of J. A. Buckley and Tony Brooks with picture research and captions.

Illustrations

LINE DRAWINGS

PHOTOGRAPHS

Acknowledgments

The author is much indebted to W. J. North, of Calartha, Pendeen, for preparing the surface plan and section from the very complex and sometimes irreconcilable originals; also for photographs and information. John H. Trounson, of Redruth, has provided invaluable assistance, by making available a large quantity of original documents from his own collection, giving much help and guidance based on his own extensive knowledge of the mine, indeed, the final chapter of the book could hardly have been written without his help. Justin Brooke, of Harrow-on-the-Hill, furnished much useful data, particularly relating to the early working of Botallack. Thanks are also expressed to: P. L. Hull, archivist, County Record Office, Truro; H. L. Douch, Curator, County Museum, Truro; Mrs M. Harvey, Librarian, Penzance (Morrab) Library; J. K. Mealor, Librarian, St. Ives; G. C. Penaluna, Scorrier; Miss Dora R. Chirgwin and Mr. W. Chirgwin, St. Just; Douglas C. Vosper, Saltash, Michael Shipp, Scunthorpe; J. P. Weeks, Manager, Levant Mine; D. B. Batchelor, Managing Director, Geevor Tin Mines; Sir Patrick Kingsley, K.C.V.O., Secretary of the Duchy of Cornwall; whilst D. B. Barton, of Truro, provided his customary useful advice, help and encouragement.

Introduction

Though not among the greatest of our Cornish mines, as measured by the criteria of size or output, Botallack yet bears a name that is the equal of any. One does not have to look far for the sources of this almost legendary reputation. Situated only a few miles from the Land's End, its engine houses cling precariously to the sides of rugged cliffs against which the Atlantic surges in rough weather with tremendous violence, making the solid rock quiver with its fury. At two places - Wheal Cock and the Crowns—the workings extend for some distance under the sea, so that, at Wheal Cock especially, the workmen were sometimes obliged to retreat in terror at the crashing of waves and boulders just a few feet above their heads. The Crowns Diagonal Shaft, which gave access to the deepest submarine workings, was a notable feature of the mine. By its means, many celebrated personalities—among them, the Prince and Princess of Wales (later Edward VII and Queen Alexandra)—were able to visit these more remote levels riding easily down and up again in a tram waggon or "gig". The Royal Visit of 1865 set the seal of fame upon Botallack, conferring a distinction which its equally romantic and far wealthier neighbour, Levant, never quite achieved. As a result, no Cornish mine has since been more sketched, painted, and generally fussed over than Botallack. Remembering what great things were done elsewhere of which scant notice has been taken, it might be possible to argue that Botallack has received more than its fair share of praise. But if such doubts arise, it is only necessary to stand atop those majestic cliffs at the Crowns to have them instantly dispelled. For here, all around, lie the evidences of an enterprise conceived and executed with skill and daring, by a unique breed of men. In this dramatic setting the combined challenge of adamantine rock and resentful sea was met and mastered, to bring well-nigh inaccessible riches of tin and copper to the light of day. The story of this achievement forms the theme of the present book. It is a story as inspiring as any to be found in the annals of Cornish mining; yet, like so many of them, ending in failure and disappointment. There is, however, reason to hope that there many yet be a new beginning for Botallack, and a future as bright, if not brighter, than its past. In the current mining revival, Levant is already being redeveloped, and it seems more than possible that eventually Botallack will be joined with it and Geevor to form a great united undertaking, bringing renewed prosperity to the ancient mining district of St. Just.

CYRIL NOALL

JULY 1970

Layout of the Mine

The group of workings known as Botallack consists actually of an amalgamation of a number of formerly separate mines, of which Botallack itself was one, the other being Wheal Cock, the Crowns, Carnyorth (alias Nineveh), Parknoweth (alias Truthwall), Park Bunny, Wheal Loor, Buzza, Wheal Bal, Wheal Hen, the Tolvan, Wheal Button and Wheal Hazard. The sett lies on the coast about one and a quarter miles N.N.W. of St. Just, and covers approximately one square mile of ground. It occupies what might be called the heartland of one of the richest mineral districts in Cornwall, for the fabulously wealthy Levant borders it on the north, and Wheal Owles, Boscean, and other celebrated mines on the south. The country rock is granite, overlain to the N.W. (i.e., seawards) by the altered killas and greenstone.

The relative positions of the constituent sections of the Botallack group are shown on the accompanying surface plan. Wheal Cock comprises the most northerly workings on the coast, with Carnyorth lying inland to the N.E. S.W. of Wheal Cock is the Crowns, famous for its cliff-side engine houses, with Parknoweth lying between it and Wheal Owles. The original Botallack mine itself forms the central section of the concern. The remaining mines were of considerably smaller size and importance, and very little appears to have been recorded of their careers as independent producers. When Botallack was reopened in 1906 after lying idle for a period, Wheal Owles was added to the sett, though, except for a little uranium prospecting in Wheal Edward, no development took place there during this last phase of activity. For this reason, the history of Wheal Owles itself is not described in this present volume.

The giant-killas junction in Botallack lies at a depth of 125 fathoms in Wheal Button shaft, i.e., at the coastline, this depth increasing rapidly in a N.N.W. direction, or seawards, owing to the steep angle of the contact of the two rocks. As a result, virtually all the submarine workings are in killas, those in granite being confined to the inland parts. Copper is found principally in the killas, and tin in the granite. As the ore shoots in the killas pitch away from the killas-granite junction at a less steep angle than the junction itself, they have to be sought at rapidly increasing distances from the shore with depth. Accordingly, when the famous Boscawen Diagonal shaft was sunk during the middle years of the last century, the angle of incline chosen was $32^{1}/_{2}$ degs. from the horizontal, which compares with an average angle of, perhaps, 60 degs. for the junction itself.[1] Because of the killas overlay, all the cliffs at Botallack are of metamorphosed rock, and the lodes which are visible in them contained copper rather than tin.

There are two principal sets of lodes in this sett, which cross each other at right angles. These run respectively in N.W.—S.E. and N.—S. directions. the latter are actually cross-courses, known in the St. Just district as *guides*. The smaller veins, whether metalliferous or not, were usually called *scorrans*; but there was also a Scorran lode in the mine, lying W. of the famous Corpus Christi. Dr. Robert Hunt observed that the *heaves* are, as a rule, irregular. Although the lodes have often continued rich when in actual contact with the guides, they have never been discovered on the further side. "This appears to indicate that the flow of fluid matter, by which the lode has been filled, was stopped by the cross-vein." The size of lodes varies in a remarkable way with their productiveness, being rich when of average width, but poor where small.

The lode arrangement at Botallack has already been described in considerable detail by Dines (1956); consequently, no more than an outline of the general position need be given here, supplemented by the plan and surface diagram:

WHEAL COCK. Wheal Cock load is found both under the land and sea, but changes course from S. 30° E. to E. 35° S. when crossing the boundary, its rather gradual S.W. underlie also increasing to nearly vertical. North, or Wheal Hen and Tolvan lodes have also been worked on in this sector.

CROWNS AND BOTALLACK. The Crowns lode, coursing S. 30° E. and underlying 12° E., has been continuously worked on for about a mile, a third of this length being under the sea. In some parts it bears the name Cudna Reeth. It connects with Corpus Christi lode, which courses, with varying strike and underlie, into Parknoweth. Narrow, or Hazard lode, is known at its southern end as Chycornish lode. The Bal and Scorran lodes have also been worked on to some extent. In Botallack, the Bunny and Wheal Loor lodes both cross the Corpus Christi.

CARNYORTH. The Nogger lode courses E. 20° S. and underlies 30° S. It has been worked on for more than half-a-mile, the western end of the workings extending into Wheal Cock.

PARKNOWETH. Buzza lode courses approximately E. 15° S. and underlies 18° S.; it has been worked on for about half-a-mile. Parknoweth or Truthwall lode with a strike E. 10° S. and southerly underlie, lies about 100 yards S. of the Buzza.

An interesting surface feature of Botallack, often overlooked by visitors, is the Bunny, where, at an early period, a succession of seven horizontal "floors" of tinstone sandwiched between layers of country rock, were removed, leaving a large depression. The first floor, being at surface level, is said to have been discovered by some of the tinstone being kicked up by passing horses. When Allen's Central Shaft was being sunk during the final phase of working the Bunny was partially filled with waste rock taken therefrom; but it is still possible to descent to the bottom in one place and enter a series of curious caverns from which mineral was extracted. Some of the floors were 40 ft. in diameter, and they averaged from 6-12 ft. thick.

1 The late Capt. W. James, however, maintained that the shaft should have been sunk at a more acute angle—45 degs.—owing to his belief that the ore-shoots were less divergent from the junction than is generally believed. If further prospecting ever takes place in Botallack, a clearer picture of the relationship of the ore-shoots to the junction may emerge.

Chapter One:
The 'Old Men' Under the Sea

The early history of the Botallack mines is obscure and fragmentary; all that can be said about them with any degree of certainty is that they are ancient, their lodes having been known and exploited since at least the year 1721. Carne, writing of Botallack in 1822, stated: "This mine was wrought under the sea beyond the memory of any person now living."[1] Almost all the records relating to these pristine operations appear, however, to have been lost, and we have little more to go on than the voice of tradition. Addressing members of the St. Just Institute in January 1882, Capt. Henry Boyns[2] remarked that the stream works in the valleys and the very extensive workings on the backs of lodes all over the district, proved that St. Just was one of the oldest, if not the oldest, tin mining district in the county. "The ancient miners in their search for tin worked precisely as the miners in Australia are working now. First, the stream-works were exhausted, then the backs of the lodes were worked as far as the water would allow them; and then to go deeper on those lodes, shallow levels were driven from the cliff or from the valley for draining off the water. Work of this kind was done before blasting powder was used in the mines. The shallow adit level driven from Nancherrow valley to Wheal Boys lode;[3] a considerable distance in hard granite rock, showed no marks of blasting." Gunpowder was introduced into Cornish mines in the seventeenth century, and produced great changes. The next stage in St. Just mining was the driving of the deep adits, commencing a small distance above the level of the sea. They contributed very largely to the successful working of the mines at later periods. Mr. Boyns' father's grandfather, who lived in the early part of the eighteenth century, was agent at Botallack, and commenced the deep adit level there. It was driven in his time to communicate with the Corpus Christi lode in the Higher Mine. Water-wheels were used for stamping, and horses for drawing the stuff.

Some interesting light on Botallack in the 1770s and 1780s is shed by a series of tin bounds setts granted by the Hon. Frances Boscawen, described as a "widow of South Audley Street in the Parish of St. George, Hanover Square" to various adventurers.[4] The earliest, dated 1776, was a grant to Thomas Sanders Allen, of Bosavern, St. Just, Gent., and David Dennis of Penzance, Gent., "to Drive and carry on a Deep Addit from the Sea, or as near to the same as it can conveniently be done on a certain Load called Wheal Hazard Load in Botallack Cliff, or on some or such other Load or Loads there as may be found proper and convenient for that purpose, as far Eastward as seventy Fathoms beyond or within the Hedge dividing the said Cliff from the inclosed Lands of Botallack afsd ..." They had liberty to dig and search after tin, tin ore and tin stuff from as far west (seaward) as the lode could be wrought, and up to twenty fathoms on either side of it. They were also empowered to take offcross drifts or adits from any level within the sett.

On November 11th 1786, the proprietors of "a certain pair of Tin Bounds called Noon Reeth Bounds situate … in the tenement of Botallack" granted a sett to James Maddern, of St. Just, Gent., at one-fifteenth dues for the lords (Boscawen, presumably) and one tenth for the bounders. A condition was that at least four men must be employed. What appears to have been an adjoining sett was granted on the same terms to James Maddern and Thomas Love, Gent., on April 18 of that year. This was described as "Carnyorth Moor Bounds & the Little Goon or Noon Reeth Bounds on the Tenement of Carnyorth."

The most interesting of these agreements, however, is that dated January 5th 1788, made by the owners of "Grills's Bonny Mine" to John Tonkin of St. Just, and partners. They were granted permission to mine for tin "throughout a certain Tyn Mine situate … on the Tenement of Bottallack … called or known by Grills's Bonny, that is to say from the carrying road in the Clift as far East ward as the Bonny field hedge, as far South as to Joyn Bottallack addit sett & as far Northward as the Tenement of Bottallack extends on the floors & beds of Tyn formerly worked by Grills & his partners." They could work Tonkin's lode, which ran through this ground and through Roscommon Clift Bounds, and ten fathoms either side of it or any other lode or scorran that might be cut when exploring the ground. John Tonkin and his partners covenanted with the lords to continue driving the adit from Botallack Cliff until it cut Tonkin's lode " & then to keep a pick constantly at work in the Adit End on said Load until it is driven to the Eastern extent of the ground above described." A minimum of five men were to be employed, the dues being one-eighth.

The Wheal Cock section of Botallack was also extensively developed at quite an early date, and its workings carried out for some considerable distance under the sea, as shown by Dr. Pryce's well known but always re-readable description of it in 1778:

"The mine of Huel-Cock, in the parish of St. Just, is wrought eighty fathoms in length, under the sea, beyond low water mark; and the sea, in some places, is but three fathoms over the back of the workings; insomuch, that the tinners underneath hear the break, flux, ebb, and reflux of every wave, which, upon the beach over head, may be said to have had the run of the Atlantic Ocean for many hundred leagues; and consequently, are amazingly powerful and boisterous. They also hear the rumbling noise of every nodule and fragment of rock, which are continually rolling upon the submarine stratum; which, altogether, make a kind of thundering roar, that will surprise and fearfully engage the attention of the curious stranger. Add to this, that several parts of the lode, which were richer than others, have been very indiscreetly hulked and worked within four feet of the sea; whereby, in violent stormy weather, the noise overhead has been so tremendous, that the work men have many times deserted their labour under the greatest fear, lest the sea might break in upon them. This proximity of the sea over the workmen, without their being incommoded by the salt water, is more wonderful than the account which Dr. Stukly gives of his descending into a coal-pit at Whitehaven one hundred and fifty fathoms deep, till he came under the very bed of the ocean, where ships were sailing over his head; being at that time deeper under-ground by the perpendicular, than any part of the ocean between England and Ireland. In his case, there is a vast thickness of strata between the mine and the sea; but at Huel-Cock they have only a crust between, at most; and though in one place they have barely four feet of stratum to preserve them from the raging sea, yet they have rarely more than a little dribble of salt water, which they occasionally stop with oakum or clay, inserted in the crannies through which it issues. In a lead mine in Perran Zabuloe, formerly wrought under the sea, they were sometimes sensible of a capillary stream of salt water, which they likewise prevented by the same means, whenever they perceived it." [5]

Steam power does not appear to have been introduced in this district until about the turn of the century. Writing in 1842, in *A Statistical Account of the Parish of St. Just, in Penwith*, the Rev. John Buller stated that the first steam engine in that parish was a small one erected at Carnyorth Moor. "It commenced working early in the month of April 1802, on the day on which the news of the Peace of Amiens reached the parish." Carne, writing in 1822, says the engine was erected in 1801. Capt. Henry Boyns (in his previously quoted address) placed the date even earlier, in 1795.[6] Something of a mystery surrounds this "first" engine. A most interesting account of a newly-erected engine at Botallack was published in the *Royal Cornwall Gazette*, of April 11th 1807, but whether this is identical with the "first" St. Just engine at Carnyorth Moor remains a conjectural point. Certainly, its date is later than those given by any of the quoted authorities; but, on balance, the author is inclined to believe that it is the same one; a view which, if correct, certainly adds to the interest of the description:

"*Improvement in Mechanics*—There is now working at Botallack Mine ... a Steam Engine of a 20-inch cylinder, on a new plan, which for simplicity and neatness of construction, and for economy in the consumption of fuel, is not perhaps to be equalled in the world by any machine now at work. The water of the Mine, on which it is erected, is kept by *three* bushels of coals, and which quantity, if doubled, has never before been found sufficient even to keep up a fire in the smallest Engine ever before erected in Cornwall. This machine, instead of having four valves, in the usual complicated form, has only one; which by the most ingenious contrivance, and the peculiar structure of the fire-place, economises the steam, so as to enable it to perform its work, with at least half the quantity of coals usually allowed for working Engines of the same size. There are several other advantages peculiar to this machine; particularly in its being converted into a *double Engine* in less than an hour, without any expense; whereas in those of the common sort, very considerable sums are expended with great loss of time, to make double. *This machine can be erected for a less sum of money than the common single Engines, and possesses all the advantages of double ones, without loss of time.* This Fire Engine may now be seen at work. It is let by contract to the Engine man at 21 bushels per week."

In 1822, Carne recorded a number of interesting details about the Botallack group, those relating to Wheal Cock being obtained from an old miner. This latter mine had been idle for several years. The adit mouth was very little above high water mark, and at very high tides the sea flowed into it. At a depth of about 20 fathoms a level nearly 100 fathoms long was driven under the sea. Its end was probably no more than five fathoms from the sea bed. In one place ore had been stoped about 12 fathoms above the level. About 40 fathoms under high water mark another level was driven under the sea for about 30 fathoms, and the whole of the lode between this and the higher level had been taken away. At 20 fathoms deeper, or 60 fathoms in all, a third level was driven about the same distance. The water in every level was very brackish, and was drawn to the adit by a small water engine. In the "Botallack Tin and Copper Mine" Carne observed how the ancient workmen had followed the ore so high as to open a communication between the sea and the mine. Whether this opening was made whilst they were at work, or the sea afterwards broke through the thin barrier which remained, was not known; it had, however, been stopped by a wooden platform on which was laid a mass of turf, and the whole covered by stones from the beach. About half spring, the sea flowed over this covering at every return of the tide. At that time, the first level on the Crown lode[7] was about 30 fathoms below high water mark, and had been driven the same distance horizontally; the 40 fathom level was driven 10 fathoms; the 65, 30 fathoms; the 85, 40 fathoms—all these being under the sea. Here again, the water was brackish, but less so in the deeper levels. At the 40 fathom level a small stream of fresh water was found. On Huel Button lode, also, there were two levels at 40 and 50 fathoms below high water mark, the first about 20, and the second at 30 fathoms in length. Although the depth of the mine was 105 fathoms below adit, the whole of the water drawn by a small steam engine did not exceed 40 gallons per minute.

That same year (1822) Dr. Forbes wrote a paper entitled "The Temperature of Mines,"[8] in which further particulars relating to Botallack occur. He gave its height above sea level as about 40 ft.; depth in May, 1822, 672 ft.; the number of men employed under ground, 150; expenditure of candles per month, 1,200 lb.; expenditure of gunpowder per month, 600 lb.; and the quantity of water discharged by the pump daily, 57,600 gal. The mine had been working for 17 years. One of the miners gave Dr. Forbes some interesting particulars about the celebrated freshwater stream. In one of the levels, at a considerable depth, this single stream had existed for a long time, "which, like the fabled Fons Aradius of the mariner, was pure and sweet amidst the surrounding brine". It flowed from the roof, and was so small as to be rather a succession of drops than a continuous thread of water. Whilst it lasted, the miners kept a bottle suspended below to collect the water for drinking; but it disappeared in the course of working the mine. Dr. Forbes measured the temperature in a number of places in Botallack. One of these was the 390 ft. level under the sea, on the lode. Beneath this there was an "old working" which had been long abandoned and was filled with water to the floor of the level above. This excavation was 10 fathoms deep, and of considerable length. The temperature of the water, which was quite salt, was 62°. The highest temperature recorded, at the inner extremity of the 510 ft. level where the men were at work, was 72°.

A third contributor that year to the *Transactions* of the Royal Geological Society of Cornwall—H. S. Boase—took as his theme "The Tin Ore of Botallack and Levant". He described how a workman from the stamping mill and burning house at Bortherras had sent him three specimens of tin ore containing copper, one of which proved to be an aggregation of yellow copper-ore and tin-stone. The third specimen, believed to have come from Wheal Hazard, proved to be a very rare example of tin pyrites. It had a compact, uniform structure, perfectly homogeneous in appearance, its percentage analysis being: Cu 31; Sn 28; Fe 6; S25; silica with a little alumina 7; and loss 3. Apart from this isolated case, the tin and copper ores were in intimate mechanical combination. Boase remarked that the copper ores were chiefly the yellow and grey sulphurets (sulphides). The tin ore was mixed with red iron stone in the vicinity of the crosscourses; elsewhere it was largely disseminated in chlorite, containing also a portion of arsenical pyrites.

The dressing processes then followed this pattern: The iron ores were rejected as far as possible in the mines, and the tin and copper ores separated from each other; when mixed, they were examined to see whether they could be dressed best as tin or as copper. The copper was spalled, picked and washed, etc., in the usual way. The tin, being "foul", was treated by a more complex process. After being cleaned of waste material, it was stamped fine in the mill, the waste water being very red and turbid, owing to the iron stone held in suspension. The ore was then buddled on an inclined plane, the iron stone, copper and tin being separated on different parts of its surface by reason of their different specific gravities, the tin, by far the heaviest, at the top. The very fine tin, being carried off by the water, was recovered by deposition in slime pits, followed by "trunking" a process similar to that of buddling. The weight of tin obtained was generally less than a tenth of the weight of stone which passed through the stamps. It was then carried to the burning house and calcined in a single reverberatory furnace capable of holding half a ton at a time. The calcination lasted 18 hours, the temperature being kept at a dull red heat to prevent the material from melting. When much copper was present, much stirring was needed to prevent "kerning"—i.e., running together. After roasting, all copper was removed by placing the ore in a cask of water, the dark blue liquid resulting being drawn into another vessel, in which pieces of iron were placed, a chemical exchange then taking place between the two metals. The calcined ore was now rebuddled, the tin separating more readily than before, owing to the chemical changes which had taken place, the most important of these being the removal of the arsenic and some sulphur in the form of vapours. At that period, the arsenic was not recovered, and its deadly fumes contaminated the countryside for some distance around. Boase stated that the precipitation process he described had been in use at Botallack and Levant for about five years.

One of the best of the early descriptions of Botallack was that given by Dr. J. A. Paris, in his *Guide to the Mount's Bay* (1824 ed.). He spoke of the Crowns as being among the most extraordinary and surprising places in the mining districts of Cornwall, both on account of the rare and rich assemblage of its minerals, and the wild character of its rock scenery. This mine—and its equally famous engine—derived their name from a group of rocks called the "Three Crowns". "Surely, if ever a spot seemed to bid defiance to the successful efforts of the miner, it was the site of the *Crown Engine* at Botallack, where at the very commencement of his subterranean labours, he was required to lower a steam engine down a precipice of more than two hundred feet, with the view of extending his operations under the bed of the Atlantic Ocean ! ! ! There is some thing in the very idea which alarms the imagination; and the situation and appearance of the gigantic machine, together with the harsh jarring of its bolts, re-echoed from the surrounding rocks, are well calculated to excite our astonishment.

But if you are thus struck and surprised at the scene when viewed from the cliff above, how much greater will be your wonder if you descend to the surface of the mine. You will then behold a combination of the powers of art with the wild sublimity of Nature which is quite unparalleled; the effects of the whole being not a little heightened by the hollow roar of the raging billows which are perpetually lashing the cliff beneath. In looking up you will observe troops of mules laden with sacks of coals, for the supply of the engine, with their undaunted riders, fearlessly trotting down the winding path which you trembled at descending even on foot. As you approach the engine, the cliff becomes almost perpendicular, and the ore raised from the mine is therefore drawn up over an inclined plane,[9] by means of a horse engine placed on the extreme verge of the overhanging rocks above, and which seems to the spectator below as if suspended in '*mid air*'.

"The workings of this mine extend at least seventy fathoms in length under the bed of the sea; and in these caverns of darkness are many human beings, for a

1. *Crowns engine houses in background, with old dressing floors on cliffs in foreground. The ore dressers, including bal maidens and children, have paused for the picture. Note the precarious wooden hoisting gear on edge of cliff at top of picture. (c. 1865)*

*2. The Prince & Princess of Wales with their party descending Boscawen
Diagonal Shaft seated in a gig. This was only months after the same gig plunged
to the bottom of the mine killing several miners. (24 July 1865)*

small pittance, and even that of a precarious amount, constantly digging for ore, regardless of the horrors which surround them, and of the roar of the Atlantic ocean, whose boisterous waves are incessantly rolling over their heads. We should feel pity for the wretch who, as an atonement for his crimes, should be compelled to undergo the tasks which the Cornish miner voluntarily undertakes, and as cheerfully performs."

The lode could be seen cropping out in the rocks beneath the engine, the ore being the grey and yellow sulphide of copper, mixed with oxide of tin; the mine had already sufficient of this to afford a very handsome premium to the adventurers. Mixed with the grey sulphide, a purple copper ore, called by the Germans *buntkupfererz*, was frequently met with. Other interesting minerals included jasper; arborescent native copper; jaspery iron ore; arseniate of iron (previously unknown until discovered in the Crown lode; it was of a brown colour and crystallised in cubes); sulphide of bismuth, embedded in jasper; the beautiful specular iron ore; haematitic iron; and the hydrous oxide of iron, in prisms terminated by pyramids, supposed by Count de Bournon to contain titanium. The district rock consisted of hornblende, alternating with slate. The Crown rock itself consisted of extremely compact hornblende, in which occurred numerous beds and veins of other minerals. These included veins of garnet, with numerous embedded crystals, being at one part almost a foot in width; magnetic iron pyrites, massive, in beds, near the engine, bluish-grey in colour, and mis-named spelter by the workmen, who probably mistook it for blende; and the true blende itself, which was found in considerable quantities. In an almost inaccessible part of the rock was a vein of epidote, distinctly crystallised, and about six inches wide; the miners, however, descended the fearful precipice without any difficulty to collect specimens for the inquisitive visitor. Axinite also occurred in veins, or beds; whilst thallite, chlorite, tremolite, and a black crystallised schorl, in which six per cent of titanium had been detected, were also found in this remarkable place.

In describing the Crown's engine, Dr. Paris unfortunately failed to give any details of its history. It is known that it was built prior to 1816; and appears to have been subsequently—perhaps in the 1830s—replaced by another engine. At all events, the engine-house depicted in Tonkin's 1822 engraving, looks quite different from the one to be seen there today. The fact that the latter has survived for well over a century in this exposed position provides a remarkable tribute to its unknown builders. An unusual feature is that the stack is placed within a corner of the house—doubtless a result of the restricted space available.[10] Half-way up the cliff above it stands another engine-house built in 1860 to drive the whim on the Boscawen Diagonal Shaft, used in prosecuting the seaward extension of the Crown's mine. Together, these massive structures, in their cliff-side setting, afford one of the most unforgettable sights to be met with anywhere on the Cornish coast.

1 Trans. Roy. Geol. Soc. Corn., vol ii.
2 Capt. Boyns had spent nearly 50 years in St. Just mines, and had been an agent in every one then at work in the parish except North Levant. The account of his extremely interesting address will be found in the *Cornish Telegraph* of January 5th 1882.
3 In Wheal Owles.
4 These documents were kindly made available to the author by Mr. G. C. Penaluna, of Scorrier.
5 *Mineralogia Cornubiensis*, 1778.
6 Capt. Boyns asserted that the *second* engine in St. Just was erected at Wheal Owles around the year 1810.
7 It seems clear from this description that the Crowns and Botallack mines had already been united at the time Carne was writing.
8 In Trans. Roy. Geol. Soc. Corn.
9 This appliance was known as a *shammel whim*.
10 See D. B. Barton, *The Cornish Beam Engine*, 1965.

Chapter Two:
The James Dynasty Begins

By 1835, the shallower workings at Botallack had become exhausted, and further search proving unremunerative, the old proprietors thought of abandoning the mine. But if they had lost faith in her, there was one man at St. Just who held far different views of her potentialities; and by taking quick and decisive action at the appropriate moment, seized control of this enterprise for himself, and thereby started Botallack on the most profitable stage of her fabulous career. It makes a dramatic and exciting story of the kind which has given Cornish mining its aura of romance. In this case, too, it is a story which until now has remained almost, if not quite unknown, locked away, with many other treasures of the kind, in mouldering newspaper files and dusty achives.

The man who stepped forward in 1835 to rescue Botallack and to make the fortune of himself and his family, was Stephen Harvey James. He was the eldest of the ten children—five sons and five daughters—of Jaketh James, of Nancherrow, who subsequently became lessee of the farm of Botallack, which had been in their possession since 1797. Jaketh James and his wife both died when nearly 90, and were survived by all ten of their children - a somewhat remarkable circumstance, in those days of high infant mortality. Stephen Harvey James was fortunate in receiving an excellent education. The schoolmaster at St. Just then was John Davey, a mathematician of first-rate ability, who was often consulted by Davies Gilbert, and by engineers from distant parts of England. Naturally shrewd, Stephen James soon became an adept at figures, and at the age of thirteen began to assist his father, who acted as local land agent for the Boscawen property, which included Botallack mine. He eventually succeeded Jaketh James in this position, and also became toller for the mineral rights of the same family and for the Hon. Mrs Robartes. In addition to these interests, he engaged in farming, an occupation which assisted in developing his physical prowess.

Even when a boy, Stephen had joined in all the village sports and became a formidable amateur wrestler. One day there was a great wrestling match on the Eastern Green at Penzance. With another St. Just youth, James Nicholas, he went to look at the contests, in which they had no intention of joining. However, fired by what he thought poor and clumsy play, young Nicholas sprang into the ring. He was met by one of the brawniest of the wrestlers, a "clubbish" fellow, who seemed pleased to punish the young wrestler of the better sort, who had essayed his skill, and mauled him about unmercifully. However, the rules were not broken by such rough play; so Stephen James could only bite his lip and hold his tongue. After a gallant struggle, down went Nicholas. In an instant Stephen was in the ring and gave a direct challenge to the unfair wrestler. Serving him for some time as he had treated Nicholas, he flung him when and how he pleased. "In for a penny, in for a pound." The amateur wrestler stuck to the work throughout the day, and carried home the first prize. It was his first and last appearance, formally, in the ring. He later found an outlet for his energies as a cavalry volunteer. One of his great feats was to lift from the ground a pump weighing eight hundredweight.

As toller of mineral dues, Stephen James acquired a great love of mining. He assisted agents in dialling and frequently made inspections of mineral areas; whilst his residence close to Botallack naturally led him to take a great interest in that speculation. On hearing that the proprietors were thinking of "knocking" the mine, he offered to purchase the sett. This was accepted; but so confident was he of the undeveloped wealth of Botallack and so determined to follow out any course he had resolved on, that he rode off at once to Edward, the first Earl of Falmouth, in order to get the purchase ratified, as he knew the vendors would, after a few hours' consideration, have withdrawn from the agreement.

In 1836 Stephen Harvey James became purser of the new enterprise, holding this important office until his death in 1870[1]. Particulars of the mine during the very early years of his *regime* are few, and hard to come by. W. J. Henwood, writing in 1843 (Trans. R.G.S.C., vol. v, p. II) stated that in the year ending June 1838, 10 tons of copper ore had been sold for £185. The total labour force at that time numbered 172. He was particularly impressed by its character as a submarine mine.

"In Little Bounds, Botallack and Wheal Cock the miners' hardihood tempted them to follow the ore upwards even to the sea; but the openings made were very small, and the rock being extremely hard, a covering of wood and cement in the two former, and a small plug for the latter mine sufficed to exclude the water, and protected the workmen from the consequences of their rashness. I was once, however, underground in Wheal Cock during a storm. At the extremity of the level seaward, some 80 or 100 fathoms from the shore, little could be heard of its effects, except at intervals, when the reflux of some unusually large wave projected a pebble outward bounding and rolling over the rocky bottom. But when standing beneath the base of the cliff, and in that part of the mine, where but nine feet of rock stood between us and the ocean, the heavy roll of the larger boulders, the ceaseless grinding of the pebbles, the fierce thundering of the billows, with the crackling and boiling as they rebounded, placed a tempest in its most appalling form too vividly before me to be ever forgotten. More than once doubting the protection of our rocky shield we retreated in affright; and it was only after repeated trials that we had confidence to pursue our investigations." One curious feature which he noticed concerned a lode which passed no less than three times from granite into slate; at every change in the granite it yielded only tin, but wherever it traversed the slate, the produce was entirely copper.

The Rev. John Buller, Vicar of St. Just, prints a few details for the year 1841.[2] The annual dues of Wheal Cock amounted only to £18; whilst there were but two employees! The dues for Botallack were £183 14s., the labour force totalling 172—confirming Henwood's figure. The latter mine possessed one draft engine, 36"; one whim, 26½"; a second whim, 19"; and four water-wheels of 25', 22', 21' and 20' diameter.

How was the mine faring financially during this period? The answer, in a word, was, badly; and to the outsider it must have seemed as if Stephen James had made a very poor bargain. Writing in the *Mining Journal* on June 14th 1843, J. Y. Watson stated that Botallack had been abandoned in 1835 on account of a heave in the lodes, after raising tin and copper worth £53,230 between 1814 and 1835. On a resumed working from 1837-41, copper only was produced worth £2,055. Another source[3] gives a markedly different account of the results achieved during this period, though the general picture of failure is much the same. According to this, the new adventurers started in January 1836, and from then to December 1841, calls of £17,500 were made. In the same period, the tin sold amounted to £13,166 and copper £3,060.

Whichever set of figures is correct, and irrespective of whether or not any tin had been raised, the situation facing the shareholders at their meeting in November 1841, was an extremely serious one, and the agent told them "he knew not where to find two penny weight of ore in all the mine."[4] Several were therefore strongly inclined to abandon the concern, but they eventually decided to continue it for a further two months, with a resolution to give up the whole if there were no improvement in that period. This resolution must have been inspired by Stephen James himself, whose confidence in the mine never wavered. His faith was soon to be justified, for it afterwards appeared that whilst they were thus discussing the advisability of abandoning the enterprise, the workmen were within two or three inches of a rich bunch of copper ore, which in twelve months was to yield a profit of £24,000. The first news of the discovery was published in the *Royal Cornwall Gazette* of March 11th 1842— that a rich lode of copper had been laid open in the 85 fathom level, its finding, as so often in mining, being a matter of mere chance. Being in entirely new and whole ground, unusual excitement had been created. The first dividend was declared in May 1842;[5] and in August it was announced that a 4 ft. lode of grey copper ore had been cut, worth £250 per fathom—this being an absolutely phenomenal value for the St. Just district, and probably never equalled there, either before or since.

In 1843, Watson stated[6] that the several lodes of the sett were returning tin and large quantities of very rich copper, the latter averaging £14 a ton, enabling the mine to make a profit of £1,000 a month[7] Since the great discovery of copper in 1841, the rich courses of this metal had returned 1,269 tons, yielding £15,906 13s. 6d. As Watson does not date these returns, they cannot be compared with those of Courtney. However, there can be no doubt that this "bonanza" afforded a most striking instance of the uncertainties of Cornish mining. An enterprise on the point of closing because of the apparent poverty of its lodes had overnight become one of the richest mines of the county. It was an achievement to arouse envy and admiration elsewhere; and, in darker days that lay ahead, the memory of that wonderful find gave Botallack adventurers the courage to dip again and yet again into their pockets for calls, hoping—but, alas, in vain—to repeat this marvellous success.

It so happened that the great copper find occurred at a time when the price of tin was very low. Accordingly, in 1843, S. H. James and Richard Davey, in "that patriotic and enterprising spirit which characterised the generation in which those gentlemen lived," commissioned a dinner service of pure tin from Messrs. Dixon and Co., of Sheffield, to induce mine agents and others to follow the example they set them, and so stimulate the demand for that metal. The exact words of the order were "as full of tin as possible consistently with hardness." Antimony was actually used as the hardening agent. The service consisted of nine dozen plates, dishes—and hot water dishes of all kinds to match—covers, cruet-sets, and all complete. The whole cost of this large service was less than £50, showing that if, in the absence of any definite tin-ware manufacture, articles could be turned out so cheaply, upon the establishment of such a branch of industry, they would be extremely cheap to make in comparison to porcelain and crockery. One doubts if this assumption would still hold good today, with the current high price of tin! In 1877 it was said the plates had been in pretty constant wear since they were made 34 years previously, but were not bulged or damaged, nor were they as deeply scratched as silver plate would have been after a similar amount of use. They were clean and sweet, and serviceable in every respect, and had proved a good investment, if only for the saving in crockery. Considering, too, how well they burnished, they could be considered as combining use with beauty.[8]

An excellent description of the mine was published in 1845 by J. S. Courtney, in his *Guide to Penzance*—a work to which reference has already been made. After eulogising the scenery, he stated that one of the engines was at the edge of a precipitous cliff, another at its foot close to the sea, and a third on a slope where it seemed scarcely possible it could have been erected. "These, with other parts of the machinery, interspersed amidst a mass of rugged green stone rocks, present a scene not likely to be met with in any other part of the world. The effect is greatly heightened should a storm, or even a small breeze blow from the north or north-west; the waves are then violently driven against the rocks, and the spray is carried even to the highest part of the cliff."

He recommended the visitor to inspect the higher engine, which drew the ore from a spot just above the water's edge to the top of the cliff over an inclined plane of wood inserted in a channel cut in the rock. This engine also drove a mill for crushing the ore. "A person standing here, at the extremity of the wooden platform, and viewing the mine at a great depth below, with the rugged rocks around, and the wide sea beyond, can scarcely avoid a feeling of terror at his own situation." It was a considerable distance from here to the lower part of the mine, using the regular road, but by scrambling down a cliffside path—"which even ladies frequently do"—it could be much lessened. At the bottom, another wooden platform fixed in the rock led to the shaft where the ore was discharged; from here it was conveyed in small waggons by a railway to a part directly over the foot of the inclined plane, to which it fell through a wooden funnel. The ore was drawn up the plane in an iron bucket. From the end of the platform a flight of steps led to the very bottom, where the largest steam engine—the Crown—raised water from the mine. "The tourist should by no means omit to go round the engine, and from thence get on the (Crown's) rock; he will thus face the stupendous and almost perpendicular cliff over which the inclined plane passes, and obtain a view which many prefer to any other part of the mine."

Although Botallack had been saved by a great find of copper, tin soon began to play a dominant role in its fortunes. The quarterly returns for July—September 1847, illustrate this point very well:

"To balance at last account, £243 1s. 4d.; cost for three months, £1,822 15s. 6d.; merchants' bills, £846 14s. 2d.; total £2,912 11s. By copper ores sold, less dues, £511 12s. 10d.; tin sold, less dues, £2,252 11s. 2d.; total, £2,764 4s.; leaving an adverse balance of £148 7s."[9]

These figures also plainly indicate that the mine had lapsed into comparative poverty again, following the exhaustion of the copper deposits. The *Mining Journal* of April 26th 1851, stated that from May 1842 to 1846, Botallack paid no less than £42,500. The mine then became poor, and made a call of £750; but during 1850 improved again, and paid three dividends of £500 each. On this resumption of prosperity a vote of thanks was passed to Lord Falmouth for his remission of dues during the period of recession.[10] The tin which the mine raised was sold by private contract—presumably to one of the local smelting companies. Sixty eight tons of copper raised during the first quarter of 1851 sold for £7 5s. 6d. per ton, realising £515 2s. The sett at this time covered one square mile. The "tin mine"—Higher Botallack—had reached a depth of 170 fathoms; the Crowns, or lower mine, was working at 150 fathoms and sinking to bring the 165 and 180 levels under it. This part was then 180 fathoms under the sea. Wheal Cock had been recently added to the sett.

The year 1851 witnessed the opening of the Great Exhibition in London; and during June the adventurers agreed that the underground agents should visit it one at a time, at the purser's discretion—doubtless to study any mechanical appliances there on display which might be applicable to mining. In August 1852, the Prince de Joinville and his royal French entourage visited Botallack and went underground where they remained some hours. They enquired closely into the various operations there, and derived some amusement by breaking the copper ore and hauling the winzes— "the Prince ... exhibiting great spirit and intelligence". On leaving, they gave a handsome gratuity to be divided amongst the agents and men.[11] These appear to have been the first of a long series of distinguished persons who visited the mine during the third quarter of the nineteenth century.

In the July-September quarter of 1852 dues on copper of $1/18$th and on tin of $1/24$th were paid, those on copper being the first remitted since they had been given up in 1848-9.[12] Leifchild, writing in 1855, noted that the share-list on December 31st 1853, showed that the greatest price paid for a Botallack share was £387, the originally paid amount of a share being £91 5s.

In an interesting little book published in 1855, entitled *Cornwall: Its Mines and Miners*, an excellent description of both the surface and submarine parts of Botallack is given—unfortunately far too long to be given at length here. The author was particularly impressed by the cliff-side footway, by which the miners ascended—"and he must have a sure foot and a strong head who can comfortably tread those ladders, round by round, the sea roaring under him, and almost flinging its raging spray after him as he gets higher and higher!" He vividly summed up the whole busy scene at the Crowns as follows: "Chains and pulleys, chimneys and cottages, posts and winding machines—seem to be scattered over the face of the whole cliff, like the spreading lines of an immense spider's web; while in some parts mules and their riders may be observed to be trotting up and down the rocky tracks, that the pedestrian visitor would scarcely dare to pass." Getting underground at Botallack was itself quite a feat: "You do not go straightly and evenly to the shaft's mouth, as in other mines on level ground. But you have to pick your way down to a small counting-house, erected on a cliff or prominence half-way between the summit of the rock and ocean. You must first go there to find the mining agent who will accompany you. What an accumulation of mining gear you must pass! Long chains stretched out over bell-cranks and posts—wooden platforms looking like battered remnants of wrecks—and yet supporting large beams of timber and heavy coils of rope. Here, there is a little creaking, crazy-boarded shed—there, a broken-down post or two—and there again, you must wind round by the rocky path amidst chains and cables and ascending loads."

He descended by ladders to a point 480 feet below the ocean, and, amongst other wonders, was shown the two wooden plugs which kept back the sea where the excavations had been carried up too high. His guide estimated the thickness of the rock at these two places as 5-6 feet and 3-4 feet respectively. The writer gave a miner a shilling for a bit of ore which he claimed to have struck out only three feet below the water! He also heard the sound of the sea above his head— "it comes like the remembered sound of a rolling surge—like the swell of the ocean's diapason from a considerable distance—partly like the sound of wind outside a house on a stormy night, but far more regular—more majestic—less wild. It has a melancholy majesty in it—it has a spiritual impressiveness in it. It does not threaten, but subdues into humility and meekness. One moment there is a harsh grating in it—that arises from the rolling up of some loose stones; and now all is melancholy and solemn again. In truth, we only hear the sound of distant waters, lashing rocks 120 feet above us."

This book appears to be the original source of the almost incredible, yet true, story of "The Blind Miner of Botallack". A man, blind from some unknown cause, became a labourer in the mine, and continued his perilous underground work for a long period, through dread of being compelled to accept parish relief. By this means he supported his family of nine children; and such was his marvellous recollection of every twist and turn of the subterranean labyrinth that he became *a guide to his fellow labourers* if their lights were accidentally extinguished. But this wonderful tale has a sad ending. On being discharged from this employment—"and they truly must have had rocky hearts who did discharge him—*heu, auri sacra fames!*"—he was engaged as a labourer to some bricklayers who were building a house at St. Ives. It was part of his duty to carry hods of mortar up to the scaffolding, from which, having taken a step too far back, he fell, and was killed almost instantly.

The *Mining Journal* of December 22nd 1855, stated that the Crowns was then producing all the rich copper ore of the mine, and mentioned a recent discovery in the 180 fathom level. Some levels were then 200 fathoms under the sea. The agents' report for March and April 1856, showed that the 180, 165, and 150 levels in Wheal Button had been driving. "In 165 level had good lode of Copper 6 feet long, but does not hold forth—are now driving cross-cut thro' the lode, can give no opinion yet, other ends unproductive." At Wheal Hazard, then, apparently, in process of re-development, the shaft, sinking, was "very troublesome"; they were not so far down as anticipated, being only 63 fathoms below adit, but believed they had gone through the worst part. The end at 100 S. from this shaft on Narrow Lode was driving by two men at 84s. per fathom, but unproductive. At the 85 level a cross-cut was driving towards Narrow Lode at 120s. per fathom. In the Chycornish section, also being re-opened, the engine was working to drain the water, which would be got out in two weeks, when the shaft would be cleared and the drained levels driven. In Higher Mine, eleven ends were driving on tutwork, five of which were opening good tin ground. There were 22 tribute pitches working here at from 5s. to 16s. in the £, the ends being more productive than they had been. In Wheal Cock, eight ends were driving and two winzes sinking on tut. Engine Shaft was completed to 135, with shaft and winze plot cut. The 120 end produced tin and copper, insufficient to pay for breaking ground. The 70 W. was promising for copper, and had left good tribute ground for 3 fathoms long.

In June, the 165 cross-cutting W. through the lode at the Crowns was reported to have found a good course of copper 2 feet wide going N., worth £50 per fathom. The lode was 14 feet wide, and they were driving N. under it to hole to a winze sinking under the 150. At Wheal Hazard they had been driving a level and taking up a winze for a footway; it would take two months more to complete the shaft. At Chycornish the shaft had been cleared and made good to within two fathoms of the 70. The Crowns cross-cut had intersected the lode at the 180 by August, but it proved poor. At the 165, however, the lode had improved in value to £70 per fathom. By October, the 180 in the Crowns was 305 fathoms N. of Wheal Button Shaft, driving at £8 per fathom, but the agents were now of opinion that the lode had, after all, still not been cut through. The 165 was also 305 fathoms N. from the shaft; behind this end, and S. of cross-cut the lode had been taken down for 7 fathoms, worth £80 per fathom. At Wheal Hazard, the shaft had been completed to the 100, and the men were preparing to put a tram-road in the 100 fathom level S. on Narrow Lode. At Chycornish, the shaft had been cleared and secured to bottom of the 80 fathom level; the levels N. of this shaft would now be cleared. Wheal Cock Engine Shaft was 12 fathoms under the 135, and had 3 fathoms more to sink at a bargain of £35. The lode in the bottom was large but poor. Six ends driving on tutwork were unproductive. By December, the men at the 180 were at last cross-cutting through the lode, which produced some tin. Others sinking under this level had broken several tons of good copper ore—this place looked very promising. Wheal Cock Engine Shaft had reached the 150; ends driving E. and W. from the bottom were poor. The 70 W. was worth £20 per fathom for copper.

On the financial side, Tredinnick (1857) gave the total dividends paid on each share to the end of 1856 as £385 5s., the annual amounts disbursed since 1846 being:

1846	1,500	—
1847-9	Nil	—
1850	1,000	£5
1851	1,500	£7½
1852	2,550	£12¾
1853	6,500	£32½
1854	11,100	£55½
1855	8,000	£40
1856	5,800	£29

The total amount being £18,250 at January 1st 1857. Another authority stated at about this time[13] that approximately £75,000 had been divided by the company. The average price received for copper was £6 18s. per ton. The machinery included two pumping engines (24 inches and 30 inches); four winding; and a water stamps of 24 heads.

In April 1857, the agents again stated that the lode in the 180 at the Crowns had *not* been cut through; in the bottom of the level there was a good pitch of copper which had been refused in the price at the last setting, and was idle. The 165 was driving by four men at £10. The lode had split into two branches, but seemed likely to join again, when good results were expected, as both parts were producing copper. In Higher Mine, Engine Shaft had reached a depth of 205 fathoms, levels having been driven N. and S. about 20 fathoms each, and promising well. In June, the agents were once again confident that the 180 in the Crowns was cutting through the lode, its value being uncertain. The winze sinking under had opened good copper ground, but the lode in the 165 had not turned out as well as expected. In Wheal Hazard, the 85 and 100 fathom levels S. on Narrow Lode were producing a little tin. Skips had been completed to the 80 in Chycornish, and men were fixing pitwork preparatory to sinking further. Eight ends were driving in Higher Mine, some opening good tin ground. Davy's Shaft was sunk 4 fathoms under the 90, the men cutting the ground and fixing timber for skips. Wheal Cock Engine Shaft was sunk 150 fathoms below sea level, the last 40 fathoms being on Tolven Lode. They were driving seven ends on it, all poor. The 70 fathom level was driving by four men 12 feet high; the lode had a good appearance in the bottom for about 10 fathoms long. In August, the 112 was driving W. on a large lode producing much mundic. A glimpse of the working conditions in Chycornish is given in the October report, which stated that operations in the 70 fathom level had been delayed for want of air. A winze sinking under the 50 had been driven 13 fathoms, and would communicate with the 70 in two months, thereby improving ventilation. At the end of the year, the Crowns was reported unproductive, except for some copper stopes under, and over the back of the 180. The agents considered the mine had not improved since last meeting.

This year (1857) saw the writing of the first of a series of reports on Botallack by Mr. (later Sir) Warrington W. Smyth for the Duchy of Cornwall Office. Smyth was principally concerned with the dues payable to the Duchy from those parts of the mine lying under the foreshore, but he had a keen eye for all aspects of mining, and his accounts form a valuable historical document.[14] Smyth noted that the best portions of the veins had, with increasing depth, to be sought for at constantly increasing distances from the shore. Thus in the deepest levels driven from the Engine Shaft at Botallack, the distance traversed in the vein before any ore was arrived at had been from 3-400 fathoms. He explained this by the fact that the lodes, which course seaward from the shore in a nearly northerly direction had been found most productive near the junction of the granite with the hard and modified slate and greenstone which overlie it. This granite-killas junction which rises to the surface inland, dips towards the sea, so that with increasing depth the granite is met with further and further out towards the N.W. The deeper levels, at 150, 165 and 180 fathoms, from surface were, without being rich, yielding a moderate quantity of copper ore, with which scarcely any tin was intermingled, although that metal was raised in considerable amount from the "old mine" under the land. Scarcely a drop of water found its way into those remote levels and what there was was fresh, arising from lateral springs in the rock. "This would facilitate the further sinking of the shaft, which ought soon to be recommenced."

Though he does not specifically say so, it is clear that he was referring in the last sentence to the Crowns section of the mine. His report of the same date (December 21st 1857) on Wheal Cock reads as follows: "(This) is a separate working, also belonging to Botallack, on a lode farther to the N.E., which during the last twenty years has yielded literally nothing. The perseverance of the Company has been rewarded at last by the discovery of a productive course of Copper Pyrites at the 70 fathom level, beyond low water mark. At both of these mines (Botallack and Cock) as well as Levant, the coast is very precipitous, and a very narrow strip, exceedingly difficult to define, would exist between high and low water mark. Beneath this foreshore copper and tin ores have formerly been raised, but from the cause above specified, the workings on ore are now much further out at sea." In other words, it was the Crown rather than the Duchy which would now be benefiting from royalties.

In February 1858, the 180 driving N. at the Crowns was still unproductive, though the first of two winzes sinking here was producing two tons of copper ore per fathom, at a depth of 5 fathoms. The 165 was also driving, and had good stones of copper ore. The agents stated: "The 180 end is now N. of Wheal Button Shaft about 325 fathoms, and expence of sinking the Sump Shaft and driving deeper levels so far N. will be very considerable, and we shall then only be at the 195 fathom level. Now suggest sinking a Diagonal Shaft so as to reach the present end (180) distance about 360 fathoms. We think it can be done at less expence than sinking Sump, and will be of great benefit to working the mine in future." At Chycornish, Engine Shaft was down 8 fathoms below the 80. The lode here was nearly perpendicular from surface to the 80, but they had not yet broken through it. An attempt was being made to cut Parknoweth Lode by driving S.

In April, the two winzes under the 180 in the Crowns had been suspended until the Diagonal Shaft had taken their place, but they had a good appearance for copper. The sinking of this shaft had already commenced. Stopes over the back of the 165 were very productive for copper. In Chycornish the 80 N. had driven 7 fathoms through a good tin lode, whilst the shaft was 12 fathoms below that level. Other parts of the mine were producing tin, and its appearance generally was better. By June, the Boscawen Diagonal Shaft had been communicated from the cliff to Wheal Button Shaft (22 fathoms), whilst its construction was also to be expedited by sinking and rising at the 20, rising over the back of the 33, driving the 50 fathom level, and rising over the back of the 65. The August report stated that the Boscawen Shaft was sinking and rising by sixteen men and six boys from Wheal Button Shaft to the 65. The 150 level had been suspended until the shaft was sunk, but the 180 and 165 were still driving N, the latter having a good lode of copper 3 fathoms long.

In his report of August 23rd 1858, Smyth wrote: "I suggested, last year, that it was time to commence sinking below the 180 fathom level; but to obviate the loss of time and expense of the usual method, the lessees have commenced an inclined plane, to be carried down as evenly as possible, from the extremest rocks seaward down to the deepest point of the mine at its farthest extent under the sea. They had already, on the 5th inst., completed 20 fathoms, and were about to attack it from several different levels simultaneously—so that it will now be important to economise the little ore left in the extreme workings, until the inclined shaft is finished." The 180 and 165 levels were both advancing, and at about the same distance from shore. None of the Crowns' shallow levels was being driven, as they had passed through the productive run of ground. At Wheal Cock, the yellow copper ore in the 70 fathom level, which the previous year exhibited a very encouraging appearance, had fallen off again.

The agents reported in October that Boscawen Shaft was sinking and rising by 20 men and 13 boys—over the 115 and 100, under the 85, over 65, 50, and 33, and under the 20. In Wheal Cock, the 125 N. had a promising lode of tin. "We regret we cannot show a better report, but from several prospective points we hope to discover something of value." By December, the 180 in the Crowns was 350 fathoms N. of Wheal Button Shaft, lode not cut through. Two stopes over the back of the 165 were very productive for copper. About 160 fathoms had been opened in the Boscawen Shaft, which was progressing faster than expected. Chycornish Engine Shaft had been sunk to the 100 level, and a skip road put in to the bottom. The lode of yellow copper in the 70 end at Wheal Cock, referred to by Smyth, had improved, being then ten inches wide. The position of the mine generally was about the same as at the last meeting.

Throughout that winter, construction of the Boscawen Shaft proceeded rapidly; and in April 1859, about 225 fathoms were reported opened. In Wheal Hazard, the 65, which had been productive, was suspended, the men being employed sinking a winze from this level to the 85. In Higher Mine, the 205 driving N. from Engine Shaft had reached tin ground gone down from the 190, the end being very productive. The 135 driving N. in Wheal Cock was producing good copper, and had an excellent appearance. The lode in the 70 end, though split, had an appearance of improving.

Writing on June 20th 1859, Warrington Smyth announced that excellent progress had continued to be made in sinking the Boscawen Shaft; but a source of great difficulty and expense had arisen from the yielding of the lode walls at about the medium depth of the mine, requiring the judicious placing of heavy timber to obviate the danger. The deepest (180) level at the Crowns was still opening northward; six fathoms back from the end a little tin was visible, although the present end, costing, £5 per fathom to cut was valueless both for tin and copper. This extreme point was about 100 fathoms in advance of the last place where a cross-cut through the lode exhibited favourable appearances for the "copper glance" ore which had formerly constituted the chief wealth of the mine. The 165 was also driving northward but without any ore in sight. At Wheal Cock, the yellow copper ore which looked so well two years before, had entirely "cut out", but in the extremity of the 70, the miners, just prior to Smyth's visit, had opened to view some ore of the same character, "again investing with an air of promise the undersea workings of this mine, which for many years past has often capriciously put in a favourable aspect and as often again lost it." At the 112 the lode had been driven on for 100 fathoms under the sea, without any ore in all that distance. At the 125 a new lode had been opened up some months before, whose appearance strongly induced him to recommend its further trial. "In the deeper workings the temperature is rather high, a disadvantage added to by the small size accorded to the levels in this district, where the custom is to work 'single handed', or with only one man at once in the end." At the 150 level, which was remarkably dry, the lode was small, but contained some "good colourless tin ore".

On the land side of the shaft, only a few fathoms inward from the coast line, a short course of excellent copper ore was working, which had added so good a "parcel" to the recent sales of Botallack as to render the undersea ore small in comparison. "The Royalty in fact accruing to the Crown has reached a very low ebb from which I hope it will be raised when the shaft above alluded to has been completed, and perhaps earlier by a further discovery at Huel Cock. For precaution's sake I visited the old shallow workings where a hole was many years ago bored through the roof into the sea, it is now stopped with a wooden plug, and the rock about it is so sound as to give no reason for apprehension." The report is rather confusingly put together; but it seems fairly clear that the rich copper "parcel" found near the coast was in the Crowns' part of the mine.

October saw Boscawen Shaft communicated from surface to 8 fathoms below the 150; they had started to lay the rail road, and all work was satisfactory. The 180 and 165 were driving N. in the Crowns, unproductive. In Wheal Hazard, the 100 and 165 were opening fair tin ground. In Higher Mine, the 205, 150, 140,

110, 90, 70, 60, and 50 ends were driving on the Bal Lode, several ends opening tin ground. The 150 W. on "Park Bonney lode" was driving, poor. Davy's Shaft was sinking under the 90 in good tin ground. In Chycornish, the 100, 90, and 80 were driving N. on the Guide, poor. The 80 E. on Buzza was producing some tin, ground hard. In Wheal Cock, the 135 was driving N. on New Lode, producing tin and copper. The 112 driving W. was poor. Ventilation was to be improved by rising against winzes sunk from the 70. The Boscawen Shaft had 40 fathoms of timber laid for rails by December, the men then being engaged in squaring and securing the shaft. An improvement was noticed in Wheal Cock at this time.

Writing in the *Mining Journal* at the end of that year, J. Y. Watson noted that the mine was in 200 shares, "and a transaction in them is a very rare thing". The dividends for 1859 were £3,000, the same as for 1858. The one declared on December 12th was the 72nd; for many years, without intermission, there had been two-monthly dividends ranging from £10 to £2 10s. per share. The same paper gave further interesting particulars of this mine on March 17th 1860. It was divided into four distinct sections—Botallack, 205 fathoms deep; the Crown, 180 fathoms deep, with levels driven 500 fathoms (sic) under the sea, rich for copper; Wheal Cock, principally copper, carried undersea to a depth of 150 fathoms; and Chycornish, tin, in granite, 100 fathoms deep. Botallack had paid £25-30,000 profits. Crowns, the richest section, had produced a profit of at least £80,000 invariably from grey copper ore. Wheal Cock had been poor during the present working, making a loss of about £20,000, but now nearly paying cost. Chycornish was "nothing remarkable". The mine had eight steam engines. Stamping was done by water power in a valley about a mile from the mine, the ore being carted thither at about 1s.6d. a ton.

The stamping of ores formed the theme of a letter written by Henry Boyns in March 1860[15]. In this, he argued that as the quality of their tinstuff had been decreasing in recent years, it would be necessary to augment the stamping power to prevent a falling-off in returns. To support his case, he quoted the following figures: in 1855-6, the average raisings were 24,000 sacks; 1857, 30,865; 1858, 35,112; 1859, 45,511. The grade had fallen from 3 dwt. in February 1859, to 1 dwt. in January 1860 on a sampling of 5,595 sacks. "The principle that Black Tin is made up to 356 lb. of Black Tin per 100 sacks at 1 dwt. 0 gr. it will make some thing short of 9 Ton 0 cwt o q o lb of Tin which is very certain that unless we can raise more than that quantity we cannot pay cost." In Wheal Hazard, the ground recently opened (with the exception of the back of the 65) was of low quality, averaging about 16 gr.; in Higher Mine ground recently opened in the S. part of Davy's Shaft averaged 1 dwt. and a quantity of ground N. of Engine Shaft still less; Chycornish nothing better. To counteract these adverse circumstances, they had during the past year increased their water stamping power from 2,000 sacks per month to 4,500. but this had still proved inadequate. "Seeing that we have 10,000 sacks in the mine and are presently rising more than we can possibly stamp, at the best, I see no alternative left us, but to Imploy Steam, I therefore recommend that we have a 30 inch Engine as early as possible, for … there is no time to lose, the summer will be fast upon us, and put her on the Narrow Shaft to pump the water, and attach 32 heads to stamp the coarsest of the stuff … As we are likely to have a large quantity of poor stuff fromWheal Hazard an incline road could be put in very easily and drawn up by the same Engine; and if the Narrow Shaft was ever wanted to work the Narrow (Lode), that could be made the drawing shaft."

In the summer of 1857, Capt. Boyns had measured the waste water and found it to be 52 gal. per minute. "Supposing that the comb works about ten hours per day, it would be about 120 gallons per minute worked over and over economically (and) will not be found a bad supply for the size comb wanted by us, and will make us just as well off as our neighbours. There is some waste water coming from Parknoweth which could be applied to an advantage in working leavings."[16]

A colourful account of Botallack appeared that year in the *Illustrated London News*,[17] the mine being described as "a work worthy of Virgil's Vulcan and the smiths of Lipari". The mules, engine houses, cliffside ladders, and other wonders were all described and, under the sea, "the sunless galleries, which no eye but that of man has seen; with treasures of buried wealth—bands of pure copper— lining the walls, and waggons full of ruddy ore rolling over the tramways, while there is not a cranny in the metallic roof, green with the ocean ooze, but is echoing to the low, mysterious, muffled sound … of the surf breaking on the shelf of rock 120 ft. above the dimly lighted recesses".

The agents reported in February 1860, that Boscawen Shaft was down to the 180—bottom—except 14 fathoms in sollars under the 150, 220 fathoms being completed for rails. Doubtless at Capt. Boyns' prompting, they recommended immediate erection of a steam stamps, the quantity of tinstuff raised for some months past having more than doubled with but a small increase in the quantity of tin. In April, it was announced that the 180 and 165 driving N. of Wheal Button Shaft were unproductive; but at each end they had cut a lode at right angles from the Crowns Lode. This would be of great importance in cross-cutting towards the parallel lodes under the sea. This cross-course was 370 fathoms N. from Wheal Button Shaft. Boscawen Shaft was sunk and opened about 300 fathoms, and railroad laid to 50 fathom level. The last two-monthly report on the mine was issued in June; thereafter three-monthly ones became the rule, the first of these covering the period July-September 1860. It showed Boscawen Shaft sunk 3 fathoms below the 180. In Wheal Hazard, the 100, 85, and 65 were driving S. on Narrow Lode, which was, however, in disorder owing to its intersection with the Spar Lode. The 85 and 65 ends were improving and producing tin. The steam stamps were now under construction, and it was hoped

3. The Crowns engine houses after the mine had closed and the timber gantry had been removed. Taken at the end of the 19th century.

4. Lithograph of Botallack Mine by J. Tonkin of Penzance. (Dated 1822)

5. *Wooden gantry which angled down from Crown engine houses into the mouth of Boscawens Diaganol Shaft. The royal visitors have just descended in the gig. Note the entrance decorated with greenery for the occasion. (24 July 1865)*

6. Wheal Cock Engine Shaft headgear in the 1890s.

would be working in three months, work having been delayed by bad weather and scarcity of masons.

Warrington Smyth, in a report dated September 22nd, stated that the inclined shaft was nearly finished. The section which, at his last visit, appeared in a dangerous condition, had been adequately secured with expensive timbering of American and Baltic balks of 16 inches square. Meanwhile, only the two deepest levels, at 180 and 165 fathoms, had been kept advancing northward in the Crowns. The first had just intersected a cross-vein, and although no ore was in sight, this feature promised to bring a change of ground, as well as offering a means of economical cross-cutting. A rise was putting up to communicate between the two levels, but the temperature was so high as to render it difficult for the men to do their full work. The ore recently raising from under the sea had been chiefly from stopes in the back of the 165, whence the vein had been nearly removed up to the 150 fathom level. The yellow copper ore of Wheal Cock, at the 70 fathom level, which formerly promised so well, had been a disappointment, wedging out on every side; but a number of exploratory galleries had brought other hopeful points to view. At the 135 level, the so-called "New Lode" was improving in character, yielding some good copper pyrites; the 125 and 112 were driving, but poor. In the 95, a level had been commenced from a series of winzes opened in the lode for ventilation, and the "branches" or veins running side by side together promised to yield some good tin ore.

In December, the agents announced Boscawen Shaft sunk 8 fathoms below the 180, lode not broken through. Rails had been laid to 100 fathoms. The end of the 165 N. in the Crowns driving S. on the cross-course at £4 10s. per fathom, had produced a large quantity of mundic. In Higher Mine, the 205 was driving N., yielding tin worth £7 per fathom. In Chycornish, the 100 was communicated to the bottom level of the old Narrow Mine. Weather had retarded work on the Steam Stamps and the Narrow Shaft. "Have cleared and secured 41 fathoms and to within 4 fathoms of the deep adit level—this has been a difficult and expensive matter".

An unfortunate gap of nine months then occurs in the transcripts of agents' reports. However, Smyth, writing early in September 1861, fills in some of the missing details: "The Botallack adventurers have been exceedingly bold in expending during the past year some £10,000 in preparations for a durable mine, such as the Inclined Shaft ... and an extensive new Dressing Floor, with large Steam Stamps, etc., for returning the tin which is their principal support from the lodes under the land. The inclined shaft is completed to the 180 fathom level, the bottom of the mine, and carried or sunk 2 fathoms deeper. The operations Under Sea, on the 'Crowns Lode' have been almost limited to this. In Wheal Cock, the high temperature and closeness which rendered the travelling of the mine a very fatiguing day's work have been much amended by the completion of some winzes or blind shafts from the 70 to the 112 fathom level. The 150 fathom level which has a depth of about 180 fathoms from the surface at the shaft is driving on the 'new north lode', with encouraging appearances as it runs seaward; and it is singular that although the works are extended so far beneath the sea, and are—in one shallow 'back'—divided from it by only some 3 or 4 feet of rock, through which a borer hole actually tapped the water, these deeper levels are perfectly dry and dusty, and the total quantity of water which has to be raised in both mines is so moderate that the exploration of comparatively very poor lodes can be carried on with an economy impossible in other parts of Cornwall."

The agents' chronicle was resumed in the October—December quarter. In the Crowns, the engine house had been built for working the Boscawen Shaft. The engine was nearly erected and boiler fixed, but difficulties arising from the position of the engine house had retarded progress, and another month would be required to get it in working order.

Their March report for 1862 proved to be an historic one, for it announced the inauguration of the Boscawen Diagonal Shaft—one of the most remarkable and famous shafts ever sunk in a Cornish mine. It will here be quoted in full, the slightly condensed transcript being conjecturally restored to something like its original form: "January, February, and March, 1862.

"Crowns. The Boscawen Shaft is working to the bottom of the mine to our entire satisfaction. We have driven through the lode at the 190 fathom level, at the bottom of the shaft, the lode 2 feet wide and worth £20 per fathom for copper—driving N. and S. from cross-cut—the lode at each end worth £20. We have 3 pitches working for copper. We have a winze sinking under the 165, and men are clearing different levels of stuff deposited during the time Pearce's Winding Engine has been idle.

"Wheal Hazzard. We are still driving the cross-cut at 100 E. and 85 W ., both very hard. Ends of 85 W. and 65 E. opening tin ground.

"Higher Mine. There are 10 ends driving, 110, 90, 80, 70, 60, are opening tin ground which will pay. We have 3 winzes sinking—are opening the ground—32 pitches working for tin on tutwork and 23 on tribute.

"Chycornish. 90 E. driving, lode worth £20 per fathom 100 driving N. and S., opening tin ground of low quality.

"Wheal Cock. We have 7 ends working. The 150 N. is driving, worth £12 per fathom for copper, but lode now disordered by slide from Eastern wall. The lode in the 135 is 1 foot wide, yielding both copper and tin, worth £5 per fathom. The 112 N. is producing tin. The 95 E. on Wheal Hen is opening tin ground. We have two pitches working over the 112, tin worth £35 per fathom.

"Our statement today is not as satisfactory as could be wished, but this is caused by the *fall in price of tin* and Crowns part of the mine being idle for 9 months.[18] The quantity of ore raised and sold for this account is small, and we would add that the amount charged in our account for labour and materials in putting the Boscawen Shaft to work and erecting Round frames for our tin dressing is at least £500.[19] We are now erecting 16 additional heads to our Steam Stamps which we hope will enable us to keep up our returns of tin during the summer months, having now at the surface 20,000 sacks of Tinstuff. We consider the mine considerably improved in the last 3 months."

1 These biographical details are from his obituary notice in the *Cornish Telegraph*, June 8th 1870
2 Buller, Rev. John, *Statistical Account of the Parish of St. Just, in Penwith* 1842.
3 *Mining Journal*, April 26th 1851.
4 Courtney, J. S., *Guide to Penzance*, 1845.
5 *Mining Journal*, April 26th 1851.
6 Watson, J. Y., *A Compendium of British Mining*, 1843.
7 In this book he also ventures the remarkable assertion that at a "former working" Botallack left a profit of £300,000. This does not appear to be confirmed by any other reliable authority.
8 Borlase, W. C., "A New Tin Scheme," in Trans. R.G.S.C., 1877, p. 228 *et seq.*
9 *Royal Cornwall Gazette*, December 31st 1847.
10 *Mining Journal*, June 8th 1850.
11 *Mining Journal*, August 28th 1852.
12 This information is taken from an MS. volume owned by Mr. J. H. Trounson, of Redruth which contains an almost complete series of transcripts of Botallack agents' reports from 1856-89. It appears to have been made by William Thomas, who became Manager of the mine in 1906.
13 Murchison, J. H. in *Mining Journal*, October 11th 1856.
14 For a detailed review of the position regarding the payment of dues from undersea mines see the present author's *Levant*. Dues from workings beyond low water mark are payabie to the Crown, Duchy royalties are limited to the foreshore.
15 MS, per Miss D. R. Chirgwin, St. Just.
16 Capt. Boyns' orthography has been somewhat modified.
17 xxxvi, 284.
18 This was probably caused by the interference with normal work occasioned by the final stages of constructing Boscawen Shaft, and the consequent alterations in winding arrangements.
19 The detailed financial statements which originally accompanied these reports were unfortunately not copied into the book of transcripts.

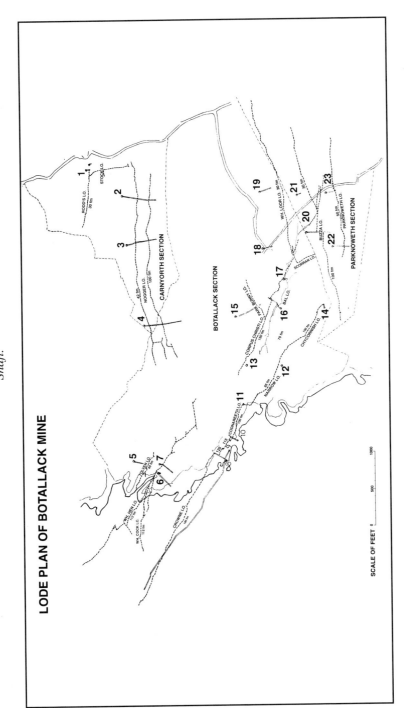

LODE PLAN OF BOTALLACK MINE

1. Rodds Shaft 2. Carnyorth Engine Shaft 3. Pearces Shaft 4. Ninevah Shaft 5. Tolevn Shaft 6. Wheal Cock Engine Shaft 7. Wheal Cock Skip Shaft 8. Wheal Button Shaft 9. Bosacawen Diaganol Shaft 10. Crowns Engine Shaft 11. Wheal Hazard Shaft 12. Narrow Shaft 13. Allens Shaft 14. Chycornish Shaft 15. Park Bunney Shaft 16. Botallack Engine Shaft 17. Davy's Shaft 18. Ludgvan Shaft 19. Durloe Shaft 20. Buzza Shaft 21. Higher Buzza Shaft 22. Flat Rod Shaft 23. Lane Shaft.

Chapter Three:
The Wonder Mine of the West

The opening of the Boscawen Shaft marked an entirely new phase in the development of Botallack; and it will be convenient at this juncture to leave the strictly chronological sequence of events to study its implications in some detail. The basic function of this shaft was to permit the deep undersea portion of the Crowns to be worked with maximum efficiency, enabling the ore to be won and hauled to surface without the necessity of driving long levels seawards from the land shafts of the mine. Starting on the cliff, it ran northwards at an angle of 32¹/₂ degs. with the horizontal, connecting with a number of levels on the way down, the lowest, at the time of its opening, being the 180, and was extended deeper and further under the sea as the mine developed. The ore was raised in a tram waggon, hauled by an engine at the top; the miners also made use of this machine for getting to and from their places of work.

The facility afforded by this tram-road to reach the bottom of one of Cornwall's most famous mines—a mine, too, so romantically situated, and with workings extending far under the sea—had the not altogether welcome effect of turning Botallack into one of the main tourist attractions of Cornwall. Just three years before its opening, the Royal Albert Bridge at Saltash came into use, permitting railway communication between Penzance and London; and so the far west of the county, hitherto only accessible by a tedious and tiring coach journey, was brought within a day's ride of the metropolis. So travellers came in increasing numbers, to visit the famous Land's End, and the almost equally celebrated Botallack mine, hard by.

It would appear that the tram was used for joy-riding from the very first day. According to a curious, semi-fictional account published in *Chambers' Journal*, the inauguration of the shaft was made the excuse for a great dinner and ball at the mansion of one of the largest shareholders. Vast crowds assembled to see the tram started; and several ladies were invited to travel in it underground, "but when they came to look at the vehicle in question, and the road which it had to travel, the determination of most of them gave way". This was not surprising; for the tramway descended across the face of a bleak cliff for a hundred yards or so, with a wall of rock on one side, and a sheer drop to the sea on the other; whilst beyond appeared a small black hole, through which the vehicle disappeared to finish its journey in pitch darkness beneath the cliff and ocean. Under the circumstances, out of the dozen fine ladies who had come to "Glendallack" to go down in the car, ten unhesitatingly declined to make the venture. "They were very sorry, they said, to disappoint the public, but the public would survive it, whereas they felt confident they themselves never should. When pressed, they took a still more dignified attitude, and refused upon the ground of religious principle. It was all very well for persons whose business lay in such places to go down there twice a day after tin and copper (or 'whatever it was') but in their own case they felt it would be 'tempting Providence'." Eventually the two bolder spirits among them—Gwendoline and Miss Blackett—took their places in the carriage. Gwendoline was engaged to be married to an elderly gentleman who was not of their party; but during the journey underground her true lover, who had somehow insinuated himself in the car, took advantage of her terrors to press his suit successfully. However, we need not trouble the modern reader with *that!*

In the years which followed, many hundreds of persons clamoured to be allowed to ride out under the sea, the popularity of the excursion being greatly increased after the Prince and Princess of Wales visited Botallack in 1865. These tourists made great demands on the services of the mine, including "an interview at the account house, a suit of clothes, and a room; a surface journey of half-a-mile, the use of an engine and tram-waggon; and the time, attention and risk of an agent, for whom there was ample other employment, for at least an hour, sometimes for two"[1] Unless some limit were placed to the number of adventurous travellers the skip might be at work all summer in the expensive and unremunerative task of lowering and raising visitors. To place some check on their numbers, it was therefore decided to ask for a donation of half-a-guinea from everyone who descended, this money to be set aside for the widowed and maimed connected with the mine. By 1871, considerably over £300 had been collected in this manner for charity. A visitors' book was also kept in the account house, in which those who made the descent signed their names and added comments on their experiences. This book is now preserved at Truro County Museum; but the page containing the handwriting of the Royal visitors of 1865 has unfortunately been abstracted by a souvenir hunter.

Several of the entries are curious and amusing. The book itself actually begins some years before the institution of the tram, and reveals that even then a number of hardy souls were prepared to make the fatiguing journey by ladders and levels to inspect the wonders of this submarine mine. Among the earliest was Thomas Q. Couch, of Polperro, who visited Botallack in August 1853. Robert Hunt, Keeper of the Mining Records, London, was there on October 2nd of that same year. On July 6th 1860, William Burrows Hambly, of Plymouth, "had the pleasure of going *underground* with his brother W.B.H., and will never forget the kind attention of his guide, Abraham Waters, & the *generous Cornish Hospitality* of the Captains, N. Hocking & Hy. Rogers, combined with the *true courtesy—common only* in this good County of Cornwall". A tribute all the more remarkable in coming from a Devonian! Miss Jane Hodge, St. Levan, Miss Ellen Laity, Sennen, Miss Eliza Thomas, and Miss Jane H. Thomas, both of St. Ives, "went to the bottom of the Mine" on November 4th 1862—using the skip, of course. Perhaps the most amusing of all the entries occurs on December 13th of that same year: "Julia Augusta Davies, Cambridge; Sarah Bedford, Penzance; John French Bedford, R.N.,—Visited the mine & went 10 fathoms below the 190, being the first Ladies who went so far. N.B. The above named Ladies left their crinolines above ground." Robert Gittings, F.R.S., &c., noted on September 7th 1864, "Descended to the 205 fathom level—the lode 3 feet wide. *Barometric* measurement to bottom of incline shaft, 1 in. 5:00, equals 1,500 ft. from Counting House level this is interesting simply as measurement in contradiction to sinking calculation." A party of officers of the Russian Navy, including two rear-admirals, visited the mine in July 1866, and gave £6. Mr. and Mrs. R. M. Ballantyne signed the book on August 17th 1868; one of Mr. Ballantyne's most celebrated books, *Deep Down*, was associated with mining in this district.[2] The last entries in the book are dated 1874.

Resuming the historical narrative, the agents reported in June 1862, that the 190 level in the Crowns had been driven N. 6 fathoms, a stope there being worth £20 for copper; but in the S. part of the level the lode had not been cut through. Two pitches over the 180 and one over the 165 were very productive for copper. The 16 new heads attached to the steam stamps were working satisfactorily.

On July 31st of that year, Capt. Henry Boyns, manager of Botallack, appeared at St. Just before a group of Royal Commissioners, headed by Lord Kinnaird, appointed to enquire into the conditions of all mines in Great Britain. The evidence collected was published in 1864 as a shorthand question-and-answer transcript in a Government publication, from which the following points have been summarised. Capt. Boyns began by stating that the incline shaft had been in operation for about six months; conveying men. Previously that part of the mine which it ventilated used to be very warm—91 degs.—but was now only about 70 degs. The ventilation took place from the incline shaft through long levels to other shafts. There were five mines in communication with Botallack on different lodes; in each there was more than one shaft, so helping to drive out the impure air. In the Crowns, the Engine and other shafts were downcast ones, and the Diagonal the upcast; but in the other sections the direction of draught varied with the wind. They were able to force air in (through levels) up to 150 fathoms by a small machine worked by a boy, who received 10s. a month. The diagonal shaft measured 190 fathoms vertically and 370 diagonally. The 180 fathom level was 400 fathoms from the vertical shaft and reached the diagonal at 280 fathoms. Beyond the point where the Diagonal Shaft reached the 180 level, ventilation was continued by winzes. In the Crowns, 50 fathoms would be driven before putting in a winze; elsewhere they had gone as far as 100 fathoms. The distance would depend on circumstances; if only one pair of men worked per day, 50 fathoms would be acceptable, but if three pairs a day were at work it was necessary to do something better. Usually there was one pair working for seven hours per day;

but if the work had to be "forced" with more men, superficial means were employed for sending in air, so saving the expense of sinking winzes. It took three hours for blasting smoke to clear from such an end.

Capt. Boyns told the Commissioners he had worked sixteen years as a miner and had had experience of a "close" end. In these ends there was a warmer atmosphere, the candle burnt less well, there was an absence of draught and "perspiration came more free". He did not believe the conditions in such ends as injurious to men's health as the evils of ladder climbing—"I think that we climb rather too fast, generally speaking". At Botallack, the men changed in the boiler houses, which was not satisfactory, but the engines being in different parts of the mine made this very convenient for them. He thought the practice dangerous, although they had had only one accident from the bursting of a boiler in the neighbourhood. This had occurred at Pendeen Consols about twelve months previously; one man was killed, but he was not connected with the engine, being out in the fields at the time. Presumably he was killed by flying debris.

Concerning blasting, the only rules they had were, constantly reminding the men on the setting days that suitable materials were provided, consisting of tamping, and a bar; and cautioning them that if they did not attend to these things, they would have no claim upon the mine (in case of accident). The bar was made of a composition of copper principally and lead, it was supposed to be incapable of striking fire. They had had several blasting accidents, perhaps not amounting to one a year. These arose from carelessness; in the most recent case, proper tamping had not been used.

Two pounds of candles were allowed each week per man, charged at 9d. per lb. The same price was charged for powder, but without any restriction on quantity. The mine bought each article at 6d. per lb.—this profiteering being common in most mines at that time, it may be added. The men contributed 6d. per man per month to the club, boys paying 3d. It was a "hurt" club, not a sick club; similar amounts were paid for the doctors, but this included attendance on all members of a miner's family. The doctors were appointed by the adventurers; there were no deductions for the barber. The men were charged a shilling each for the composition-tipped bar, which contained about sixpennyworth of copper.

Capt. Boyns was then asked by one of the Commissioners (Mr. Holland) "How are the men drawn up in your mine; in waggons?—Yes. We have a railroad and a carriage to take the men up, but without a break; it is drawn up by a chain; we do not think it safe, and the men do it at their own option; we do not warrant it; we cannot do that without having a break to the wheel." Questioned further, he agreed it was a common tram waggon drawn up by a chain. The men liked it; there was a great difficulty in keeping them out. All the men could be raised by it from the Crowns, which was not one-fifth part of the mine altogether.

Since the apparatus had come into use for raising the men, they were able to perform a third more work, and for one-third less money than previously; "that is partly from economy of toil and partly from ventilation".

Capt. Boyns stated he was aged 42, and had been an agent fourteen years. "I am still quite strong for labour." Asked further about the fan boy, he stated that if the men neglected to engage one when this was necessary, they could be "spaled" (fined) but this was rarely done; he had himself done it but twice in his life. One of the Commissioners (Mr. St. Aubyn) then took up again the matter of the men's safety when riding in the wagon without a brake, and asked "But how can you feel justified in allowing the men so to come up if you do not consider it safe?" Capt. Boyns replied, "We say to the men, 'If you do it, you do it at your own risk,' that is how we justify ourselves." Pressed further, he stated that "that matter has been attended to and a carriage with a break to it to take eight men is now working with the greatest safety". It seems strange that this information had almost to be dragged out of the witness. The new carriage did not solve the safety problem, however, owing to its brake being only semi-automatic in action; this led, in the following year, to a terrible tragedy at Botallack.

On August 1st, Stephen Harvey James, purser and manager of the mine, appeared before the Commissioners. He stated that they employed between 320 and 340 men underground, the total, above and below ground (including women and boys) being over 550. He confirmed that the mine had got very hot before the Diagonal Shaft was sunk; without it, they could not have followed the ore much further down. There were now no close ends, as far as he knew. They had never had ends where a candle would not burn. He had known only one workman to suffer from the heat. He was called John Waters, and worked in the worst end of the mine for years, "but I think that he is as good a man as we have now." He had suffered a little from shortness of breath, but this had now passed away. He was aged between 50 and 60 and resided in Church Town. Mr. James went on to describe the system of bringing air into long levels by the fan machine, worked usually by a boy. The force of the air, conveyed by iron or zinc pipes, was such as would blow out a candle. They usually started using the fan when the end was about 40 fathoms from shaft; the greatest distances driven by its aid was 70 or 80 fathoms; once it went on to 100 fathoms. The boy had to blow constantly whilst there was a man in the end. Two "corps" of boys were employed, relieving each other like the men; they rarely worked three "corps" (cores) in the mine. Each "corps" worked no more than five hours, though they might be seven hours from the surface. The first "corps" went down at seven-thirty and came up between one and two o'clock, when the second took over; but in many cases they only worked one "pair" of men, not having men enough to do more. They could work cheaper with a single pair than with two, and cheaper with two than three. When extra men were put on the fan still gave sufficient ventilation. Mr. James was asked, "What security have you that the boy continues constantly blowing?" He replied drily, "If a man in an end did not find sufficient air coming in, he would take out a rope's end."

The men usually paid the boy, but this depended on the bargain that had been made. Regarding the ventilation winzes, the draught would come up or down, depending on the surface wind. If it went up, it would not ventilate the end to a very great extent. Doors were sometimes used to send air into an end. The tut-men and tributers were required to bring their deads to shaft; they would not be paid unless they had cleared their work. The men would not be spaled— "I do not think you can spale any men in this place, they would be off to another place; they are just as independent as yourself. All the spaling that you can give them is to say, 'If you have not completed your bargain altogether we will not pay you.' We cannot spale here, the men are masters here, and they have been masters for years." The men came from many places in Cornwall, but Botallack had been in want of labour for many years. Asked if he had taken any steps to induce them to come from another part, the witness replied, "Perhaps we have quietly. If you want men you dare not say so in the mine. Our men are remarkable for their independence. And there is another thing, our men all work single handed; we have not two men in an end here at a time." If the work was let in "pairs", one man came in the forenoon to work the end, and the other in the afternoon. "He holds the borer with one hand, and beats with the other, and when the hand gets tired with the hammer, the man changes it. That is a reason why the eastern men cannot work with our men here, they must all go double-handed. Single-handed men get more money; two men single-handed in an end will get as much as three double-handed men." This was true except for extremely hard rock. Ore was raised principally by tut work men. "When we had the rich bunch of ore in Botallack I never set one tribute pitch, it was stoped at so much a ton. We made £50,000 profit there, by setting the ore by the ton, and I do not think that any man made more than £4 a month by it, so that the adventurers had the whole of the proceeds. It is only where you have a good bunch of ore that it would answer to break by the ton but we are now breaking all the ore … by tut-work, at so much a fathom. Our ground is very rich, generally, and subject to what the miners call 'scotches'. It would go abroad, perhaps, into a wall of 8 or 9 feet long, and would turn out 10 or 15 tons of ore, worth £15, £18 and £20 a ton, and we have had £25 and £28." The tribute men worked principally for tin.

Their gunpowder came principally from Kennel (Kennal) Mills, near Penryn. It was the common sort of powder; they had recently tried another sort, which was sent out by Thomas Davey, but their miners did not like it. Their supply of candles amounted to about fifty dozen a week and they had used two tons of powder in the last quarter. The women and girls did not contribute to the accident club, but many of the surface men did. It was altogether voluntary, even with the underground men. They had a man some years ago who refused to pay to the club—"and I think that day fortnight he was buried". There was also a death club, which applied to every man working in the mine. If Botallack had been the last mine a man worked in, and his subscription was paid up, his widow, mother, sister or other representative would be entitled to a shilling from each of the men. The accident club account was never balanced, so there was never any debt or credit; the adventurers paid the men as they went along. Five shillings a week was paid in case of accident, until they got better. A man blinded was paid "as long as he lives, and the mine lasts". There was no distinct club fund: it did not pay, and he thought they had better turn it over—presumably to the general account of the mine. This happened fifteen years ago, when they had a number of accidents. Asked how many accidents they had had in the last three years, witness replied, "There was one man killed entirely through his own folly, and we have had two or three others who have shot themselves"—i.e., by blasting. One of these men had been blinded. There were then only about six pensioners on the club, and one of them only worked in the mine for a short while, perhaps a month.

James said he had introduced pulverised sand for tamping and oak sticks, about 2 feet long, to replace the iron tamping bars. Thereafter they went seven years without an accident; but "a man who had just come in, out of stupidity, or, perhaps, laziness … had taken up some stuff from the bottom of the level and it exploded. He had but one eye and he lost that". He thought the oak stick sufficient for everything except a hard drawing hole. The men in Botallack always used the oak stick, for which they were charged nothing. If they were found charging a hole without it they were dismissed. Rather curiously, James made no mention of the composition bar, mentioned by Capt. Boyns. They occasionally used cartridges, instead of powder, in a wet place. He described the Kennal powder as very large, "like peas just broken in two". Scarcely any of it would stick about the hole, as would be the case with a finer powder; for that reason they considered it better.

The average wages for both tut-men and tributers was about £3 5s. a month. The girls on the copper floors got a shilling a day. Boys began work at ten years of age; none of them got under 7s. or 10s. a month, but the underground boys got more. From ten to sixteen years of age this went up to 20s. or 25s. The young men were considerably more reckless than the older ones, "and you will find that all the blind cases around the parish have been occasioned by young reckless fellows. It is a very rare thing to hear of a steady elderly man meeting with a misfortune".

Asked what price ground they got, witness answered that in Wheal Cock, where it was not so hard, the amounts varied from £6 to £9 a fathom, but in the Crowns, where it was softer, it was perhaps £4 or £5 a fathom. In Chycornish one man and a boy had broken 13 fathoms in the last month. Single-handed men used $^7/_8$ inch borers, whereas two men would use a one inch borer. A great many were not more than ³/₄ inch; they were all cast steel. Re-questioned about the men's health, James said when the mine was hotter than now, he knew one miner who had been working in the 180 fathom level not less than ten years, and when he left, he was as fine and healthy a looking man as could be; he went away to another mine and got cold, and had not been so well since. Now, the air was so good in the mine that he had heard some of their people say they were glad to have a great coat to get into a corner to smoke their pipe.

The men were paid half in notes, half in gold. Witness had brought home £1,275 the previous night to pay tomorrow. He did not think men were obliged to go to the public houses to change their £5 notes. Little credit was given at the public houses, but too much at the shops. He thought once a month was often enough to pay people. Subsist was given at every pay, but not before it. They would be giving £40 or £60 tomorrow to people who thought they wanted something. "If they were good men we should subsist them at once. Our list of subsist is made out now, and the pay is made out. The setting will begin at two o'clock exactly, and as I begin the setting the clerk and surface agent begin the pay, and in an hour or an hour and a half the setting and pay is all over; every man is paid and has gone about his business by about three o'clock or a little after."

From these detailed accounts we gain a rare insight into the working of Botallack at this period.

The *Mining Journal* of October 17th described a picnic which had recently taken place at the bottom of Botallack. A party, composed of Messrs. S. H. James, jun., Richard Thomas, A. Chenhalls, N. Holman, Lewis, John Holman, F. Holman, with Capts. John Rowe and John Boyns, were taken down "expeditiously and safely, in three parties, by the wagon, and soon proceeded to discuss a very substantial dinner, at which her Majesty's health, the purser's (Mr. S. H. James) and the engineers of the shaft (Capt. John Rowe and Henry Boyns) were drunk, with proper *éclat*. After breaking for themselves some specimens of copper ore, they inspected the 180 and 165 fathom levels, where so much riches were formerly discovered, and, satisfied with fatigue and sightseeing returned again to the surface, instructed and delighted by the trip". No doubt this little jollification was arranged to satisfy the principal shareholders that their money had been well spent on the new shaft.

In December, three men were driving a cross-cut through the lode at the 190 S. at the Crowns, but the Spar part of the lode had not been cut through. In Wheal Cock the tin ground had lengthened and the lode become larger, but the quality was not so high. Warrington Smyth, in his 1862 report noted that this northern portion of Botallack had greatly improved beneath the sea during the last year. A small lode sunk through by winzes between the 95 and 112 fathom levels, which looked well for tin, had a further opening yielding very handsomely. The best example he had seen (in the back of the 112) was worth about £100 per fathom. "I trust that this encouragement will induce the adventurers to persevere with this mine seaward."

It was on April 18th 1863, that Botallack suffered the disaster for which it is now so well known. This occurred in the still comparatively new Boscawen Shaft, and resulted from the breakage of the chain by which the miners were raised and lowered in the tram waggon. To understand what happened, it is necessary to have a clear picture in one's mind of the manner in which this incline tramroad worked. The entrance to the shaft lay in the cliff about 30 feet above high water, the winding engine being situated 80 feet higher up. From this engine to the bottom of the shaft ran a narrow gauge (2 feet 7½ inches) tramway over which was lowered and raised a small waggon or skip for mineral, with a separate, specially designed carriage for conveying men. Only one set of rails was provided, the dimensions of the shaft having been kept very small to save expense in cutting through the hard greenstone rock. It actually varied from 5 to 12 feet in width, the roof being about six feet high. There was thus very little room to spare for the carriage, but all due precautions had been taken for the men's safety. The seats were arranged in tiers, one behind the other, so ensuring a uniform height of about four feet for both carriage and men when the latter were seated. About fifty feet below the winding-engine house was a landing-place where the miners got in for descending and landed on arriving. The carriage, made in 1862, by Holman & Son, of St. Just, ran on four small wheels, like a railway waggon, and was allowed to descend the $32\frac{1}{2}°$ incline (a fall of 3 feet 3 inches per fathom) by means of a chain attached to the engine, which then hauled it up during ascents. This chain was fastened to the underside of the carriage, and ran over wheels at the bottom and sides of the shaft to ensure smooth working. There were nine curves in the shaft, and at these places horizontal wheels, called rollers, each 4 feet 10 inches in diameter, were fixed to keep the chain in position and reduce the strain upon it. This chain consisted of a strong inter-linked cable running the full length of the shaft, the first 100 fathoms being of ⅝-inch best charcoal iron, the second 100 fathoms of ⁹⁄₁₆ inch and the remaining 207 of ½ inch, thus allowing for the increase of weight and strain with depth. The total length of chain was 407 fathoms. The length of the tramway in the shaft, measured from the surface of the ground to the 190 fathom level was 363 fathoms. The mineral waggon weighed about 8 cwt. and carried a load of about 16 cwt.; but the men's carriage was about 14 cwt. when empty, its full loaded weight on the day of the accident being computed at 2,894 lbs.

The carriage or gig in which the men rode was made of iron, 6 feet 10 inches long, 2 feet 5 inches wide, and 20 inches deep. It was provided with a safety-catch which operated automatically during ascents only, which worked in this fashion:—attached to the under-side of the gig was a very powerful steel spiral spring to which was connected an iron rod running in a groove, with a loop at the other end fastened to the drawing chain. The iron rod moved back and forth, according to the difference between the tension of the chain and the elasticity of the spring. Connected with the iron rod, by levers and link-work, were two pairs of eccentric cams, which projected downwards from the bottom of the gig on a level with the hollow part of the tram rails. These were so arranged that while the chain was tight the iron rod remained in a forward position, keeping the cams clear of the rails; but when the chain slackened, either by surging or breaking, the spring drew the rod backwards, causing the cams to grip the rails and so halting the vehicle. To prevent the cams acting when not required during descents through reduced tension of the chain, a second part of the catch, called the brake, was introduced. At the side of the gig, by the back seat was an upright handle—actually the long arm of a straight lever. From the short arm a movable rod ran along the bottom of the gig to the end of the spiral spring. This contrivance enabled the spring to be held in a permanent state of tension and its operation upon the safety catch prevented, the handle moving in a rack and being under the control of the "brakesman" sitting by it. In practice, the brakesman *always* held the lever in his hand even during ascents, releasing it instantly in case of emergency. When the carriage was descending with no one on board to hold the handle, the clutches were prevented from gripping the rails by a catch-spring, which held the main spring back; it was placed on the side of the truck, near the lever-handle, and provided with a notch into which the handle could be placed. It was partly to prevent the lever from falling back into the notch of the catch-spring (as sometimes happened when going round curves) that the brakesman was required to keep the handle in his hand. Along the side of the rails ran a signal-wire, to which the men gave three pulls when they wished to be drawn up, and two when they wanted to descend; this caused a bell to sound in the engine-house.

The Boscawen Shaft communicated with two levels at which the men landed to proceed with their work. One was the 135 and the other the 165, the latter being the terminus for the carriage, so that all miners working at lower levels had to ascend on foot to this point before they could ride to surface. The tramroad itself extended to the 190, but this lower section was only used for transporting materials. The rule of the mine was that first comers should be allowed to ride to surface before the others. If any men happened to be waiting at the 135 to go up, it was their practice, as the carriage passed them, to reach in and apply the brake, stopping the carriage, and then pull the signal-rope to re-start it when they were aboard. The ascent occupied generally about a quarter of an hour.

On the day of the accident the miners descended the shaft as usual at 7 a.m., and prepared to ride to surface again at 2 p.m. on completion of their "core". One group came up safely, and the carriage descended for another. The normal load was eight men, though sometimes a boy was accommodated as well. On this occasion, eighteen miners were waiting, two or three of them boys. It was decided the carriage should first convey eight men and a boy, and then return for the remainder, who, after the skip left them, sat down and awaited their turn at the 165. Suddenly these miners heard a sound similar to a gunshot, and something rushed past them down the shaft, but so quickly that they saw nothing but a few sparks. As soon as they had recovered from their fright, three of them descended to find out what had happened to their comrades. About three fathoms above the 190 they discovered the boy lying dead with a fractured skull; he appeared to have been violently jerked from the carriage. A fathom below they came upon a man, also dead, his chest crushed and ribs broken. Next they found a father and his son, both lifeless, under the carriage, which had struck the shaftsmen's brace, forcing it back some distance. It had then stopped about eight feet from the bottom, where it got across the rails. One miner was still inside with his head hanging out, while all the remaining occupants were discovered lying upon one another at the bottom of the shaft, where they had been thrown. None had survived this terrible fall, and some of the bodies were shockingly mutilated. As a contemporary broadsheet put it,

> Each one was injur'd fearfully,
> Bruis'd, broken, smash'd and dead;
> A sickening spectacle! for some
> Had lost part of the head.

Some effects of the accident were immediately observed in the engine-house; and Capt. John Boyns descended with a party of men, who found that a $^9/_{16}$ inch link in the chain had broken about 70 fathoms above the 165 fathom level. They connected the broken chain by a rope, and shortly before midnight five of the bodies were sent up in a waggon, and after that the other four. They were taken to the account-house, where their underground clothes were changed. The bodies were then washed and cleaned and taken to their homes on boards. Their names were: John Chapple, married, Nancherrow; John Chapple (his son), single, Nancherrow; Thomas Wall, married, North St. Just; Richard Wall (his son), single, North St. Just; Michael Nicholas, married; John Eddy, single, Botallack; Peter Eddy (his cousin), single, Nancherrow; Thomas Nankervis, single; and Richard Williams Nankervis, aged 12.

John Chapple lost his life by doing a good turn to another miner. According to the rules, he had been entitled to a seat in the carriage at the time of its first ascent. He took his place, but resigned it at the request of Thomas Wall—a son of one miner and brother of another who were killed—on his saying he wished to get to surface earlier to attend a neighbour's funeral. Among the group at the 165 who sat awaiting the tram's return was Thomas Nankervis, of St. Just. He had just put his little brother, Richard Williams Nankervis, into the carriage as the ninth "extra" passenger; but a few minutes later heard the vehicle roar past to destruction. Recovering from his shock, he went down with the two other men who made up the first search party—"to go and see after those I knew to be killed"—and so found his brother's body a few fathoms below the 190.

At the inquest on the victims, Capt. John Rowe, one of the mine agents, stated that the chain which had parted was just thirteen months old, and had been specially made for use with the Botallack carriage. Examination of the broken link, showed that the iron was of good quality, but had been weakened by "surging"; that is to say, three or four rounds of chain were upon one another on the cage, and then the top round had suddenly slipped on one side and strained the link in question, causing it to break. Capt. Rowe, the inventor of the machinery by which the men were riding, then gave a detailed description of the brake and expressed his view as to why it failed to operate. Had the brake handle been pulled when the chain parted the "grippers" which it controlled would have come into action and seized each rail in its narrow part by the claws with which they were fitted. However, both he and Capt. Boyns had searched minutely for traces of claw marks on the rails, but had found absolutely nothing; hence it must be assumed the brake had not been applied. In the bottom of the carriage was a sliding loop in which was the spiral steel spring which operated the gripper levers on either side of the vehicle; whilst thus in the loop or guard the brake could not act; but if the brakesman had been holing the handle in his hand, ready for instant release, there should not have been the slightest difficulty in halting its descent. He therefore believed the men had lost their lives by the handle being in the loop, so that when the chain snapped they could not immediately release it, and then became paralysed with fear as the tram hurtled with increasing velocity—a hundred miles an hour, according to one authority—down the shaft.

The brakesman on that fatal journey was Thomas Wall, aged 45, described by Thomas Nankervis, who had himself suffered such a sad loss by the accident, as a steady man. He recalled how Wall, as he got in, always used to put his hand on the brake; and that when they started on this last fatal ascent the brake was out of the loop or catch. Another witness, however—James Eddy—stated: "I have a son lying dead from the accident; if I had been in the gig, or if Thomas Wall had the lever in his hand, my mind tells me that my son would be alive now. I feel so much confidence in the gig that I am sure the handle was in the loop."

Capt. Tyler, R.E., later conducted an offcial enquiry into the accident, the results of which were published in 1864. He made some minor criticisms of the winding gear, and also of the tramway, which was in good order, but a little re-adjustment was required between the engine-house and the shaft entrance. Some additional rollers were required, however, if only to facilitate inspection, cleaning and maintenance. "At present the ascent and descent are attended with considerable difficulty, in consequence of the irregular character of the excavation and the slimy condition of the rock the rails and the sleepers." Capt.

7. Workmen constructing the concrete bases and wooden frames for the Buss Shaking Tables in the new Botallack mill. (1907)

8. Dressing floors & calciner being prepared for re-opening early in 1908. The stack was an old one which was to be re-used.

9. Botallack Count House in 1907/8 with traction engine trailer on right of picture.

10. *Mine buildings including workshops, garages and smith's shop. The pond, a reservoir for future dressing purposes, is in the centre . Note the typical mine wheel barrow. (1907/8)*

Tyler described the special braking system as "an ingenious substitute" for an ordinary block brake, which would not have acted on so steep an incline.

The chain had given way on a previous occasion when hauling up a mineral waggon, but had never failed with the miners' carriage. The brake had therefore not been tested in that contingency, but had otherwise worked very successfully —"so much so, indeed, that the miners had acquired undue confidence in the working of the incline, and had been led to indulge in tricks and experiments which occasioned much risk to their lives—such as allowing the truck to run down and then stopping it suddenly, requesting the engine-man to lower them at extra speed, jumping into the truck while it was going at speed, and over-loading it to a serious extent. As many as twelve miners are stated to have ridden up in it at one time instead of seven, which is the greatest number it ought to convey, in order to save the trouble and delay of making a second trip".

Capt. Tyler's account of the scene at the start of the last journey is vivid, and worth quoting in full: "About three o'clock in the afternoon of the 18th April, eight men and a boy got into the truck at the 165 fathom level, for the purpose of ascending to the surface. The man who took charge of the break, Thomas Wall, was on his feet, leaning back against the front end of the truck; and the boy, Richard Nankervis, sat on the back of it, with his feet dangling over the end; but the remainder were sitting in it in the usual manner. Thomas and Henry Nankervis, two brothers of Richard Nankervis, were present when they started, and the latter, Henry, cautioned one of its occupants, John Eddy, to hold his brother Richard round the waist, while the former, Thomas, remonstrated with Thomas Wall, the acting breaksman, as to his position with regard to the break-handle. He observed to him that 'he had not got fair play for the break', and on receiving the reply, 'all right, namesake,' said again, 'Take care, you have not got room for the break, Richard's (his son's) shoulder is too near the break handle.' Thomas Wall said again 'all right', and they started towards the surface, with the break-handle out of the notch in the catch-spring."

After remarking that no one in the waggon had survived to tell what had really happened after the chain broke, Capt. Tyler suggested that the long portion of chain which remained attached to the vehicle might have prevented the spring from causing the clutches to grip the rails; whilst from the conversation between the men prior to the start it may well have been that Wall was not well prepared to apply the brake by hand at the critical moment. It was actually found to be out of the notch of the catch after the accident; but would probably have been jerked out, in any case, by the very violent blow which the waggon received when it came into collision with the timbers near the 190 level. Portions of the truck, which was strongly constructed, were slightly bent by this blow; but the brake still acted perfectly when Capt. Tyler tested it near the 165 fathom level, though the spring did not act on the brake very well.

To prevent a recurrence of the disaster, he recommended that the chain be replaced by a wire rope; that a tramway with a rising gradient be provided at the 190 level to reduce the speed of a runaway carriage; that the catch-spring be completely removed, a brakesman then accompanying the carriage on descent as well as ascent, holding the handle in his hand; that a second brake of the same type be added and that a regular brakesman be appointed, to prevent all irregularities in the working of the incline. Capt. Tyler thought this last recommendation of prime importance, observing that although Wall, the acting brakesman, was described as a steady and experienced man, "the accident would not have occurred if he had exercised full care in the working of the break-handle that he was temporarily in charge of."[3]

In June 1863, Boscawen Shaft was reported sinking 23 fathoms diagonally under the 190. The lode here had not been cut through, but it was being worked on in the 190 N. In Wheal Hazard, a cross cut E. (at what level is not stated) had communicated to the old Narrow Mine. In Higher Mine, Davy's Shaft was sinking under the 130; whilst Narrow Shaft had been taken up and secured 20 fathoms under adit. They were laying tram road in the 135 E. at Wheal Cock preparatory to driving the end. The tin ground over the 112 in this section was about 22 fathoms long, but not of very rich quality. However, the mine generally had improved for tin since last account, but not for copper. In September, the agents for the first time referred to the 200 N. from Boscawen Shaft in the Crowns, which was in four fathoms, driving a cross-cut through a promising copper lode. A winze was sinking under the 190 N. to communicate the 200. A cross-cut was driving W. at the 90 level in Higher Mine towards Scorran lode. Sixty pitches were working for tin on tut and one on tribute in this section, by far the most active part of the mine.

In his report of November 17th, Warrington Smyth referred to the recent accident, which, he noted, had but little checked exploration of the mine in depth—a fact confirmed by the agents' statements, quoted above. However, until the chain which caused the mishap was replaced (in October) by a strong wire rope the men were not allowed to be drawn up or lowered by machinery. The inclined shaft had been continued more than 22 fathoms below the 190, but on one side of the lode. The 190 level had been opened above 80 fathoms N. and S., and although the lode had a fair proportion of ore near the shaft, Smyth regarded it as showing a great falling off from the upper levels. The 180 was not driving, whilst the 165 cross cut was slowly advancing N.E. towards Wheal Cock, but had so far intersected no new vein. He stated, rather gloomily: "With the exception of a couple of 'pitches' from which a little Copper ore is raising, no further work is carried on under the sea, and the large returns made by the mine and constantly yielding a handsome profit are obtained from the tin in the land portion of the Sett." Bad news, indeed, for the Duchy office, but the reverse for Lord Falmouth! Concerning "Botallack Wheal Cock", he noted that the junction of the several lodes had produced an excellent bunch of tin ore from the 95 to the 112 fathom levels, from which good returns would be made, but it continued to no great distance, and the deeper levels (135 and 150) had not yet disclosed anything sufficiently good to promise for the duration of the mine. He concluded: "I have for some time pressed on the Managers the importance of having a good Map, and am glad to state that a thorough survey is now making by a very competent person, Mr. Henderson, C.E."[4]

In December the agents reported the 205 driving N. from Boscawen Shaft, where the lode had produced good copper. The winze had been communicated from the 190 to this level, giving additional ventilation so that the ground behind could be stoped to prove the lode. In Higher Mine, the driving of the 80 and 90 E. towards Durlo Shaft had been suspended until the adit end E. was cleared and the water taken up. Davy's Shaft was sinking under the 140, whilst Narrow Shaft was taken up and secured to the 90. An interesting development in Wheal Cock was the "New Shaft", which had been cut down about 22 fathoms from surface, and was sunk five fathoms under the 70 fathom level producing a little tin and copper. The 85 was driving E. towards this shaft.

The decision to sink New Shaft arose from a suggestion made by Capt. Henry Boyns, and detailed at length by him in a "Report for the Future Working of the Wheal Cock Part of the Botallack Mine."[5] In this, he stated: "In (Wheal Cock) there are three main lodes which have been wrought on for mineral, namely, Wheal Cock, Wheal Hen and Tolvan. These lodes W. of Wheal Cock Engine Shaft intersect each other at different points. The first and largest deposit of mineral was found from the surface to the 30 fathom level W. of Engine Shaft and shallower as it went E. It was caused by the intersection of a small branch from the western wall with a dip W. and which is seen down in the cliff. About 100 fathoms W. of Engine Shaft, over and under the 70 fathom level, the Wheal Hen and the Wheal Cock intersected each other and made a deposit of copper ore, which is worked away. At the 112 fathom level the Engine Shaft which is sunk on these lodes, intersected the Tolvan, and over the 135 and 125 fathom levels both E. and W. of shaft were productive of tin and copper till they separated. About 100 fathoms W. of Engine Shaft at the 112 fathom level the Tolvan lode intersected the Wheal Cock and Wheal Hen lodes, and made the deposit of tin which we have been taking away the last two years. This intersection reaches from the 112 to about 4 fathoms under the 80 fathom level and is about 20 fathoms long with a western dip. The 135 fathom level is within 10 fathoms of the tin ground at the 112, and the 150 about 30 fathoms. It remains still a speculation what those levels will do till the ground be opened. The lodes separate from each other as they go down. The winze now sinking under the 112 fathom level is in the most productive part of the lode which is 7 or 8 fathoms deep and opening slight tin ground. The 112 and 97 fathom levels are driven W. of intersection upwards of 30 fathoms and are very poor. The ends driven E. are hard and poor."

"The shaft proposed to be sunk is 22 fathoms E. of Engine Shaft and is down to the 70 fathom level; it is small, hard and crooked and turns E. after an end. To make this a hauling shaft we must cut it down and make it good to the present bottom and then sink it to the bottom of the mine, which is about 80 fathoms deeper. To discharge the western part of the mine through this shaft by our present tramroads we must stope down the 112 and 135 fathom levels, put in tramroads and trip plots, and the bottom level must be driven from Engine Shaft E. and trip plot cut. To put the stuff to stamps by tramroad there must be a shaft tackle about 10 fathoms high, or it must be carted and a new Whim Engine had with skips and skip road, 200 fathom deep, complete."

He estimated this work would take about three years, and cost £3,000. The principal object was to work the eastern part of the mine, "as there is nothing in the western part at present in my opinion that will warrant us to make such an important alteration". The eastern ground, however, had been proved very satisfactorily in the killas. He thought the speculation lay in the neighbourhood of Wheal Hen Shaft adjoining Carnyorth Mine. Wheal Hen Shaft (then, apparently, disused) was said to be 100 fathoms deep. It should be taken up to adit level to clear the water and for ventilation. "This shaft is in the midst of cheap ground and a cross-course a few fathoms W., so that either of the lodes N. and S. can be reached very conveniently, and is also at a proper level on the surface to tram the tin stuff to the steam stamps and *can be worked by the steam whim without any new machinery.*"

By March 1864, they were preparing to sink Boscawen Shaft under the 205. In Higher Mine, Davy's Shaft was sinking under the 150, opening tin ground, and old Durlo adit E. was being cleared and drained. The New Shaft at Wheal Cock had been cut down and made good to adit level, with 2 fathoms to sink to hole to the 85, and a rise over the 100 against the shaft. The June report announced Boscawen Shaft sunk 5 fathoms under the 205. The 205 level was 24 fathoms N. of Boscawen Shaft, and the 205 S. 25 fathoms, lode not cut through. The 190 N. was advanced 60 fathoms from the shaft, the men cross-cutting through the lode. "As far as we can see, we value lodes at £100 per fathom." The agents concluded their report by stating: "Tin raised since last account is in excess of any preceding quarter, but from the great drought, the produce from our Water Stamps has fallen 20 tons of tin & from a breakage to the Steam Stamps it was idle one week." September saw Boscawen Shaft sunk 16 fathoms under the 205. The 205 S. was 30 fathoms S. of the shaft; it had been driven through an elvan course, and looked well for copper. In Wheal Hazard, the 65 W. was producing a little tin; this level had been communicated to Narrow Shaft. Five levels driving E. on Wheal Loor in Higher Mine were all opening fair tin ground. In Wheal Cock, the lode in New Shaft, sinking, was poor. The agents complained again of the continued drought, which had led to an accumulation of 50 tons of tin at the water stamps. The prospects for copper in the mine were not so good, but for tin they were excellent.

Smyth, writing on November 21st of that year, announced that the workings in Wheal Cock had been temporarily suspended in consequence of the very low price of tin, but in the Crowns the incline shaft had been sunk 14 fathoms below the 205. This level had been driven some distance N. and S. without any good result, but in the 192 N. about 60 fathoms from shaft a cross-cut E. across the lode had shown it from 6-7 feet wide, and containing about 2 feet wide of excellent grey copper ore. This had given rise to sanguine expectations, but further cross-cuts were needed to prove the length of orey ground. A good admixture of tin, however, made it appear a promising discovery. A cross-cut E. at the 165 was 80 fathoms out from the lode, but had not intersected any of the veins expected to be seen there.

If Wheal Cock had indeed been suspended, as Smyth stated, the stoppage must have been a very temporary one, for in December the agents reported the 135 end E. here poor, New Shaft sinking under the 100, lode poor, and twelve pitches working for copper and tin on tribute.

By June 1865, Boscawen Shaft had been sunk 30 fathoms under the 205. The 205 N., driving, had struck good copper worth £15-20 per fathom. In Wheal Hazard, Narrow Shaft was sinking under the 70 at £13 per fathom, ground much improved. They were cross cutting at the 80 to come under this shaft, and also driving a side tie on a lode supposed to be Park Bunny; this would take six months to complete, "and when down will cut off nearly the whole of the timber ground in the adit level N. of the Narrow Shaft". In Chycornish, a winze sinking under 90 E. was producing a little tin, and the 80 E. on the Bussa opening tin ground. Five ends were driving in Wheal Cock, the 125 W. producing a little tin. During three months, a total of 1,080 fathoms 9 inches of ground had been opened in the mine, 157 fathoms 4 inches of these in shafts, winzes and ends, the remainder being stoped on tut and tribute. During the same period 48,000 sacks of tinstuff had been stamped.

On July 24th 1865, Botallack witnessed the most notable event in the whole of its long and colourful history. This was the visit of Their Royal Highnesses the Prince and Princess of Wales (later King Edward VII and Princess Alexandra)—when not only the mine itself, but St. Just and west Cornwall generally were *en fete* in honour of so memorable an occasion. The Royal party, who were cruising in the Royal yacht *Osborne*, were guests for a few days of John St. Aubyn at St. Michael's Mount. On the morning of the 24th they arrived at Penzance pier, where the shipping was gaily dressed with flags and bunting, and drove through the decorated streets in a carriage drawn by four greys. After a brief stop to allow the Princess to name the newly-built Alexandra Road they passed through the outskirts of Newlyn, and from there drove across the peninsula in glorious summer weather to St. Just, where a warm welcome awaited them.

When the party reached Botallack, the purser and other officials greeted them. The account-house was decorated with a triple arch over the doorway, and a detachment of Volunteer Artillery formed a guard of honour nearby. A second detachment, under Capt. Bevan, was stationed near the Boscawen winding engine to control the crowds of sightseers. A great cheer was given when they arrived, accompanied by the Duke and Duchess of Sutherland, the Earl of Mount Edgcumbe, Lady de Grey, Lord and Lady Vivian, and others. At the account-house, the party took refreshments and attired themselves in underground clothes. The Princess and Lady Elizabeth St. Aubyn then rode in a donkey chaise along the narrow mules' path towards the mouth of the shaft, while the Prince and others walked behind, while a band played "God Save the Queen" and "God Bless the Prince of Wales". Half way down the cliff appeared the head of the shaft, the gaunt upper works and wooden platforms hanging over deep chasms, while far below the waves surged against the black seaweed-covered rocks. The whole length of the platform was kept clear for the Royal party, and on their arrival they were greeted by another cheer. Above, on every attainable projection and eminence "men and women clustered like gay flies on the giant cliffs, leaving immense gaps here and there, where no foot might venture save that of a bird".

The carriage which was to convey them into the mine—apparently the same one which had been involved in the recent disaster—had been gaily dressed in scarlet trimmed with yellow fringe, and in front carried a square lamp with three candles, the interior being fitted up with head-cushions and rests. The five ladies of the party had been provided with stout boots and gloves, but the ride promised to be so easy that the Princess retained her earrings and bracelets. The Princess and Mr. St. Aubyn, the Prince and Lady St. Aubyn, who made the first trip underground, looked a little anxiously down the platform at the shaft's mouth, perhaps recalling the fearful tragedy of only two years before. However, after some explanation and reassurances, the Princess stepped into the skip, compressing her dress to suit the tiny seat, and her host sat by her. The Prince handed Lady Elizabeth to the second seat from the front and joined her there. On a signal being given the skip started on its journey to the accompaniment of many cheers. In another minute the carriage was lost to view, moving all the way down at a very easy speed of three miles an hour. In the shaft, candles had been fixed at intervals, and at the 145 fathom level they passed between a double row of lights which made quite an illumination.

The road for the first few fathoms was damp, and as the visitors ducked to avoid a projecting beam or to pass under a piece of very hard rock which had not been removed to save expense, drops of water occasionally ran down their bent necks. Lower down, however, the ground became almost dry, and the atmosphere warm, the heat being felt by all. Their passage down through the little tunnel was varied at times by a sudden sharp turn round a corner, or the sight of gigantic beams, girders and planks where the lode had been stoped away. At the 205 fathom level, the skip halted. Here was a roomy plat and landing-place, with a cistern to catch the small quantity of water which percolated to this part of Botallack—"no more than a thirsty horse could consume"—but its drip-drop sounded very cool and refreshing. The visitors did not remain here, but continued to the bottom of the skip-shaft, down a much darker and more uninviting hole than that at the surface. Capt. John Rowe, their conductor, kept his hand on the safety-brake all the way down to reassure his somewhat nervous passengers.

At the shaft bottom, the visitors were greeted by Capts. Henry and John Boyns, and Capt. Hocking. From this point they reascended to the 205, and were taken to the end there, which ran for many fathoms in a northerly direction. In after years, Capt. John Boyns graphically described his experiences with the Royal party that day:

"I shall ever esteem it a privilege … to have had the honour of conducting our own Duchess[6] through the 205 fathom level of the Crown's Mine. I think I may fairly aspire to a greater honour than that of merely acting as guide and protector, and say that I gave Her Royal Highness her first lesson in practical mining. The first object of interest … after we left the shaft-plot, which is 2,400 feet from the surface, was a tram-waggon full of rubbish, and it was explained to the Princess how much labour is involved in hauling useless stuff to surface in order that the valuable ore might be worked and extracted. The tram-waggon being near the tram-hole could be easily laden with this rubbish, and the process was shown and an explanation given of the connexion between the tram-hole and the winze to which it led. We then approached a point where a lode had been cut out, and it was explained that any copper or tin which once existed there was now gone and quartz and iron alone remained. Then a winze sunk for ventilation attracted the notice of her Royal Highness; and its object, the great use it proves to the miner, and the communication it forms with other levels, were spoken of … About nine or ten fathoms further brought us to the end of the level, and the Royal party were face to face with the difficulties of breaking the ground … Here tools were in readiness, and these having been examined the Prince broke some of the ground, the Princess did the same, as did other noble ladies and gentlemen in succession. Each one broke copper ore for herself or himself which I have little doubt will be treasured as memorials of their visit to the depths of Botallack.

This is one of the hottest parts of the mine, and the fact was explained to the Royal party, as well as the means which will be adopted to lessen the heat and improve the ventilation. We retraced our steps towards the shaft and … where level and shaft unite all the visitors sat down; all seemed very glad to have a glass of champagne and without a hint to that effect, cordially drank 'Success to Botallack'."[7]

In giving these reminiscences, Capt. John Boyns omitted one charming little story which, however, he related to R. M. Ballantyne when conducting that gentleman on a visit to the Crowns, who subsequently published it in his *Personal Reminiscences of Bookmaking*. When about to begin his duty as guide to the Royal visitors, it suddenly flashed across the mind of poor Capt. Jan that in the excitement of the occasion he had forgotten to take gloves with him. He was about to lead the Princess by the hand over the rugged floors of the levels. To offer to do so without gloves was not to be thought of. To procure gloves 200 fathoms below the sea was impossible. To borrow from the Prince or the Duke of Sutherland was out of the question. What was he to do? Suddenly he remembered that he had a newspaper in his pocket. In desperation he wrapped his right hand in a piece of this, and thus covered, held it out to the Princess. She, innocently supposing the paper was held out to be looked at, attempted to read. This compelled Capt. Jan to explain himself, whereupon she burst into a hearty fit of laughter, and, throwing away the paper, took the ungloved hand of the loyal but bashful miner.

The skip made four trips altogether to bring other members of the Royal suite to the bottom of the mine. Eventually the signal was given from below to wind up, and in less than ten minutes the carriage emerged with their Royal Highnesses aboard, and they were once more greeted with hearty cheers by the waiting crowds.

1 *Cornish Telegraph*, August 23rd 1871.
2 Actually, with North Levant.
3 This account of the accident is based on the report in the *Royal Cornwall Gazette*, April 24th 1863; a broadsheet, *The Botallack Mine Tragedy*, printed by J. O. Harris, Hayle, n.d., but probably 1863; and the <u>*Report on the Conditions in Mines*</u> ... 1864.
4 These plans still survive, and partly form the basis of the diagrams in this book.
5 MS., per Miss D. R. Chirgwin, St. Just. The spelling, etc., has been regularised here.
6 Princess Alexandra was, of course, Duchess of Cornwall in addition to being the Princess of Wales.
7 Contemporary but undated MS. transcript from the *Cornish Telegraph*, per Miss D. R. Chirgwin, St. Just.
   It is interesting to record here that in October 1968, the present writer was allowed to examine the very hammer with which this beautiful and popular Danish Princess broke off her copper specimens in Botallack more than a century before. It is now owned by Miss D. R. Chirgwin, of St. Just, the grand-daughter of Capt. Henry Boyns who was one of the agents who welcomed the Royal visitors at the mine. Deeply cut in the metal on its side is the inscription "P. & Ps. of W. 1865." Miss Chirgwin described Capt. Boyns as a conscientious miner. "He used to say to the men in the mornings, if they were very early, 'Good morning'; if they were late, 'Good day'."

Chapter Four:
Turn of the Tide

The agents reported in September 1865, that Boscawen Shaft had been sunk to the 225, and they were now driving N. at the bottom of the shaft to communicate with a winze sunk from the 205. Good copper had been found, but the lode was not cut through. Rich copper ore had been found in the 205 N. In Wheal Hazard; Narrow Shaft was sinking off the lode, very hard. They were also driving E. and W. on Spar lode at the 100 from Narrow, both opening tin ground. In Higher Mine, a crosscut W. at 170 S. was driving to cut Spar lode, end very wet. In Wheal Cock 14 tribute pitches were all paying well. Because of the dry season, they had been unable to return the usual quantity of tin.

On October 27th, Warrington Smyth reported: "The copper ore discovered last year has proved to be insignificant in amount, the 205 fathom level has been driven a long distance N. and S. without success, until on the 11th inst.—the day of my inspection—some good portions of grey copper ore began to appear in the Northern end, and this promising appearance I am informed still continues. The bottom of the shaft is 20 fathoms deeper, but there is no ore in sight." (It is curious to note that this account of the Crowns does not agree with that given by the agents in September.) "At Wheal Cock, which was last year thrown idle, two levels, the 92 and 135, are driving Westward but without anything of value in them, and 5 'pitches' for tin have been set to work, chiefly about the 112 fathom level, from which returns will accrue to the Crown."

The agents stated in December that they had communicated the 225 to the winze sunk from the 205, and also driven a cross-cut through the lode. The lode was going N., worth £100 per fathom for copper. In driving the 205 N. a little copper had been found; the lode here was thought to be one of the Wheal Cock lodes. In Narrow Mine, Narrow Shaft was sinking under the 70 on a rich vein of tin; they also had a rise against this shaft over the 110. In Higher Mine, Davy's Shaft was sinking under the 150. In general, the mine had considerably improved since last account.

March 1866, saw Boscawen Shaft sinking under the 225, the lode having a very promising appearance. Three winzes were sinking under the 225, whilst in the level itself, driving N., they had taken down copper for 4 fathoms long, nearly all worth £100 per fathom. The lode over the back was mixed with a considerable quantity of tin. In Wheal Cock the 135 was driving W., producing a little tin. A cross-cut was driving at 100 W. of Shaft towards Tolven. The 95 driving W. was producing some copper; it was hoped to communicate this end to Wheal Button lode. The agents observed, "we can raise the usual quantity of tin if thought advisable, but wretchedly low prices are ruinous to us". By June, Boscawen Shaft was sunk to the 235. Men were stripping down the sides of the shaft under the 225 and putting in railroad. A winze sinking under the 225 had been holed to shaft, lode producing a little copper. The lode in the end of the 225 driving S. was disordered; they were sinking a winze under the 205 to communicate with this end. Six ends were driving in Wheal Hazard, but the section was not looking so well. In Narrow Mine, Narrow Shaft was still sinking under the 80 off the lode, and they were also sinking under the bottom of this shaft preparatory to its holing on the Spar lode. In Chycornish, only two ends were driving, one opening tin ground, the other poor. In Higher Mine, a number of ends were opening tin ground of varying quality. Davy's Shaft was being cut down and secured to the 180. Seven ends were driving in Wheal Cock, the 95 W. being the only one to value. "The mine has considerably improved for copper. Tin as last reported. On account of low price of tin and copper, we have not broken so much mineral as we could have." This last statement is confirmed by the fact that only 895 fathoms of ground had been opened that quarter, as compared with 1,041 the previous quarter.

The agents' September report disclosed Boscawen Shaft sinking 6 fathoms under the 235. A cross-cut driven through the lode at the 235 had cut some rich tinstuff. The 225 N. had driven through 20 fathoms of good copper ground followed by 4 fathoms of good tin ground. The most important item in this report, however, read as follows: "Carnyorth. This mine has been purchased and added to Botallack, and we are now remodelling the Stamps and Stamps' floors, repairing Shafts, changing lifts, clearing and repairing adit, laying Tram Roads at surface, opening levels, and laying Tram Roads underground. The 135 is driving E. of Engine Shaft, opening tin ground. The 124 and 135 W. are driving. The 199, 88, 64, 42, and 30 are driving W. of Pearce's Shaft, all opening tin ground. There are 11 pitches working for tin on tutwork, and 6 on tribute."

Carnyorth Mine, which forms the N.E. part of the Botallack sett, appears to have been largely underwritten, when an independent concern, by Messrs. Bolitho & Co., of the Mount's Bay Bank. A sketch of its history, published in the *Cornish Telegraph* of February 24th 1869, shows that in the early part of 1852, the adventurers in Spearne Consols (for whom Messrs. Bolitho were bankers) decided to re-work Carnyorth, which was included within Spearne Consols sett as a separate mine, but under the same adventurers, and from the commencement of Carnyorth accounts in July 1852, Messrs. Bolitho were treated as the bankers. In September 1862, the accounts showed a balance of £815 19s. due to Messrs. Bolitho, and subsequent accounts revealed gradually increasing indebtedness. In May 1866, it was determined that the mine should be discontinued, and its affairs wound up. Accordingly, a petition for this purpose was presented to the Stannaries Court on November 14th 1867, by the company's purser.

At the time of the meeting in May 1866, the mine was held in 2,023 shares, reduced from 2,048 by relinquishment, the number into which the mine was divided at the commencement of the Carnyorth adventure. The accounts then showed a balance of £1,843 19s. due to the bank. The purser was appointed to head a small committee for winding up the mine, and they sold the setts and materials to Botallack adventurers.

In his report of November 16th 1866, Smyth stated: "The promising appearance which I described in my report of October 1865, as existing in the deepest and most distant part of the 'Crown lode' continued to look well, up to within a few weeks. About 14 fathoms in length of a large lode, 10 feet wide, with a good orey portion of 2 feet, were actually opened in the 225 fathoms level; but during this autumn the vein has much fallen off both in this and the 235 fathoms level, entering, as it would seem, on a 'country' less favourable to copper ore. A little tin is being raised from the 205, and some also from Wheal Cock; and but for the very low prices to which both copper and tin have been reduced by the pressure of foreign imports, the mine would have been doing very well."

The account for December quarter read as follows: 1866 Dr. To Labour cost, £4,225 1s. 8d. Carriage, £339 7s. 11d. Coals ex Ships, £574 13s. 2d. Merchants' Bills, &c., £1,215 8s. 11d. Purchase of Carnyorth, 1st Instalment, £243 15s. Rents, £101 15s.—£6,700 1s. 8d. Bal. brought down, £369 11s. 2d. Bal. in favour of ads., £208 15s. 1d.—£578 6s. 3d. 1867 Cr. By Copper ore sold, January: 98 t. 13 c. 2 q. £1,144 2s. 3d. Less Dues 1-18th, £63 11s. 3d.— £1,080 11s. Tin dressed but unsold £750. Sundry credits £293 19s. 7d. (Botallack). Tin sold 117 t. 9 c. 1 q. 27 lb. £6,049 18s. 6d. Less dues 1-24th £252 1s. 7d.—£5,797 16s. 11d. (Carnyorth). Tin sold 4 t. 19 c. 3 q. 19 lb. £269 7s. 6d. Less dues $^1/_{24}$th £11 4s. 6d.—£258 3s. Balance £369 11s. 2d.—£6,700 1s. 8d. Bal. credit of Advts. last account £578 6s. 3d.—£578 6s. 3d. Bal. £208 15s. 1d. This account was presented on February 20th 1867.

By March 1867, Boscawen Shaft had been sunk to the 240 fathom level, having intersected the Wheal Cock lode. It was now, however, apparently separating from it, so the agents advised the sinking on this shaft to be discontinued until the levels had been driven further N. The new 240 level was driving, producing a little tin, whilst a winze from the 235 to the 240 had been holed. In Wheal Hazard, Narrow Shaft had been communicated to the 100; they were now sinking the shaft below this level. Only two pitches were working in Chycornish. The 205 and 190 ends driving N. in Higher Mine were opening good tin ground, whilst Davy's Shaft was about complete to the 190. The 130 level had been recently holed to workings from Wheal Owles, the lode producing a little tin. No explanation of this curious circumstance is given; but as it came out at the enquiry into the terrible Wheal Owles disaster of 1893 that the plans of that mine had been wrongly kept for a great many years—no allowance being made for magnetic variation—the error probably did not lie with Botallack in this present instance. This event had later repercussions, as will be seen.

In June, Henry Boyns drew up a report on the mine's steam and water stamps. From this, it appears they were paying a rental of £40 a year to S. H. James, jun., for "leavings" and stamps erected on his ground. They were also paying Kenidjack lords (9 heads) £2 9s.; Lord Falmouth (6 heads) £6 6s.; Lord Falmouth (6 heads, leased) £11 11s. "The late Mr. Jaketh James' stamps were two 3 heads stamps (which) have since been altered by the Avs and made 6 heads but on one stream of water; in the Summer months of no service. On this Comb the Burning house is built and a Tin house for dressing the whole of the Tin of all the Stamps." The mill stamps had been built on the land of S. H. James, jun., about ten years ago, for which the rent was £30. "The large leavings is a piece of ground where formerly was a very small 3 head stamps, since taken by Botallack advrs. The Stamps and Comb have been removed and made new from a 3 head to 6 heads and the piece of ground laid out in an Extensive leavings to take in the work from the river (?) and the leavings of the mill 9 head stamps, for which the Ads. formerly paid £50 per year, but for some years past £40." Boyns thought these rentals in urgent need of revision.

For the period of six months ending in June, the water stamps had stamped 10,042 sacks of tinstuff and 3,814 of roughs. The expense of dressing the tinstuff with leavings was £308, or £3 1s. 3d. per hundred sacks, and of the roughs £86, or 45s. per hundred, giving an average of £83 6s. 2d. Total cost (including rent, &c.) came to £539 15s. 8d., or £3 17s. 10^{1}/2d. per hundred sacks, the rent being 7s. per hundred. By comparison, 68,491 sacks stamped in steam stamps cost £475 2s. 9d., or 13s. 10^{1}/2d. per hundred, coal being charged at 15s. per cwt. From this, it is clear, contrary to what might be expected, that steam stamping was far more economical than water stamping. At Carnyorth, the steam stamping of 12,500 sacks cost in dressing expenses, with leavings, £113 19s. 4d., or 18s. 2^{3}/4d. per hundred.

On June 15th 1867, the *Mining Journal*, in a whimsical mood, spoke of Botallack and Wheal Owles as "directed by pursers who, if they are seldom underground, have the eyes of Argus, and can tell at a moment the exact state of a hundred different points". Botallack at that time employed 600 persons, and Wheal Owles 300.

In September, the 240 N. from Boscawen Shaft was driving on a promising lode of tin and copper. A rise over the 90 in Higher Mine was expected to hole to Durlo Mine. At Wheal Cock, 11 pitches were working for tin and copper on tribute. There were 17 pitches working for tin on tutwork and one on tribute in Carnyorth. It appears that both purser and agents were dissatisfied with the results achieved at Carnyorth; and Capt. Henry Boyns prepared a series of "Reselousuns" for consideration by the adventurers at a meeting held at Penzance that month.[1] He proposed three courses of action: first, that the western end should be pursued with vigour, as they had been doing, employing about 20 men in opening the mine and stoping all the tin they could to meet expenses—this part was then barely paying labour cost; second, offer that part of the speculation, with the sett to a new company—"at present she is in good working order and a very fair speculation"; third, with the present price of tin do nothing but drive ends and employ (Carnyorth) steam stamps principally to stamp the Wheal Cock foul stuff, the expense of dressing in the water stamps being so very high. Boyns also complained that he and his fellow agents were being denied many of the facilities which they needed in working this large mine. "We have not but one Cost Book in Botallack that contains the Cost and that is locked from us … We have no reference to bill, price and quantity of Tin … and consequently must be ignorant of necessity (of) … what we should be very familiar with (which) we should judge is not found in another mine in the county."

Such grumbling as this usually indicates that things are not going well; and, indeed, that quarter Botallack made a heavy loss of £2,828 19s. 7d. Mr. S. H. James sought to explain matters to the shareholders in a letter dated November 20th 1867, stating that "in consequence of the short supply of water at the Stamps we have been unable to return our Tin, the estimated value of which is £2,000, and at Carnyorth during the last year our outlay in bringing this mine to its present state, including the purchase money, has been about £3,000". True through all this was, the fact remained that the tide of good fortune, which had set in so strongly for Botallack in the early 1840's had at last turned; the long, slow decline of Cornish mining, punctuated by several hopeful but always transitory revivals, had begun. The advent of hard times was clearly seen and somewhat quaintly recorded by a correspondent of the *Royal Cornwall Gazette*[2] later that year: "Botallack has set its back to the wall, and its front to the miners' foe—low prices. Half a regiment of human moles and bees toiled early and late last quarter. The moles burrowed at such a rate that in a year they would drive and sink just five miles of ground; and bees in the accont-house, on the floors, and in 20 different occupations, strove to make cells and honey; yet for their very lives they could lay by nought for winter."

This December account was, indeed, a melancholy one, the adventurers deciding to stop the account dinners, and temporarily suspend operations in Wheal Hazard. However, in the Crowns they were sinking under the 240 N. and S. of Boscawen Shaft, both producing tin and copper. Two pitches were working for copper under the 225 N., where the lode was very rich; but as all metal there would be exhausted by the end of the month, the agents recommended this part should be let on tribute. In Higher Mine, a rise over the 90 had let down all the water from Durlo Mine. Having communicated Botallack to Durlo Mine, the agents advised erecting a winding engine on Durlo Shaft, put in a skip road and make good to the 110; "here we could make use of a wire rope taken from Boscawen, could also lay Tram Road at surface from this shaft to Steam Stamps". In March, 1868 a cross-cut driving through the lode at the 225 S. in the Crowns was producing copper, tin and jasper, ground very hard. There were 6 men working on tribute over the 240, and two pitches over the 225. In Higher Mine, 65 pitches were working for tin on tut and 11 on tribute. Operations had been resumed in Wheal Hazard, three pitches working for tin on tut at the 65 E. In Chycornish, one solitary pitch was working for tin on tribute. In Wheal Cock, several winzes were sinking and three levels driving. No mention was made of Carnyorth. "In this mine we have already opened more tin ground than we can take away in 12 months. Most of the men are employed in opening up the mine. We recommend that a 12 head axle be added to our present stamps."

At the account held on August 19th 1868, the affairs of the company wore a more cheerful aspect, a profit of £618 16s. 9d. being achieved against a loss of £519 0s. 5d. the previous quarter. Included in the returns were 103¼ tons of tin, which sold for £5,572 18s. 11d., and an unspecified amount of copper for £746 2s. 1d. The cross-cut in the 225 S. in the Crowns had been driven through a lode of copper about a foot wide, since when the level had been driven S. about 5 fathoms and again cut the lode, which was about 9 feet wide, 2½ feet of this being tinstuff of fair quality. The 205 was driving N. in Higher Mine, ground hard and producing a little tin. The 65 W. in Wheal Hazard was driving on a promising lode, with stones of tin. The 135 was driving W. on Tolven lode in Wheal Cock, then in a disordered state. In Carnyorth the adit was being cleared N. on the Guide. The recommended new stamps axle, with the addition to the dressing floors, had been completed.

In November, an increased profit of £891 12s. was announced, £500 of this being divided. The most interesting part of the agents' report was that dealing with Carnyorth. Here a cross-cut was driving S.W. on Pearce's Shaft towards Trevelyan's lode; they also had a rise over the 30 against the New Shaft sinking near the Trewellard Boundary, which was in good tin ground. Men had been clearing adit level E. of Engine Shaft and N. of the Nogger lode on the Guide, and taking up a surface shaft preparatory towards working the eastern part of that section.

The *Mining Journal* of November 28th reported that during an "awful thunderstorm" lightning struck the engine house, cleaving the spring beam, a balk of timber 9 inches square, and knocked the stair to pieces, with the windows, roof and stack. "The fluid went down the shaft at 50 fathoms, striking H. Boyns in the arm and rendering H. Lanyon speechless. They thought a gun had been fired at them." The lightning ran down altogether 300 fathoms, and along the tram 300 fathoms more, striking R. Angwin in the foot and W. Tresise in the chest. All the men underground received a severe electric shock, whilst "the ozone was suffocating". No death occurred, nor injury to the ironwork of the engine. A man called Archer, working at the stamps engine, was knocked backwards, and the arms of the round buddle machine were knocked away.

The "good old times" seemed to have returned again at the February 1869, account, when as many as 45 adventurers dined together to celebrate a profit of £2,357 6s. 2d. on the quarter and a dividend of £10 per 200th share. The agents' report showed all parts of the mine very active, particularly Higher Mine, where there were 65 tutwork pitches for tin and 14 working on tribute; but in Carnyorth heavy rains had caused a suspension of operations in the eastern part. Everyone was in good humour at this meeting, and "not the least interesting part of the harmonious and . . . instructive chat over the walnuts and wine was the way in which the health of the agents"—H. and J. Boyns and J. Rowe—"was proposed."

The *Cornish Telegraph* of February 24th 1869, gave the following interesting summary of Botallack's achievements during the preceding year: The ground broken measured 4857 fathoms 2 feet 2 inches, or 5½ miles, 6 feet high, varying in width from 2 feet to 8 feet, and worth for mineral £5 14s. 3d. per fathom. The tinstuff raised was 186,676 sacks (14 gals. to the sack) or 20,720 tons; and the copper ore 370 tons, from ground yielding about 4 tons 7 cwt. per fathom. The tinstuff gave 424 tons 19 cwt. 0 qrs. 8 lb of black tin. These realised £27,749 0s. 3d., leaving a profit on the year's working of £4,353 12s. 2d. The debt against the mine at the beginning of the year caused by the purchase and putting in order of Carnyorth, was £1,104 14s. Dividends paid totalled £2,500, and a credit balance remained of £748 18s. 2d.

At the next account, held in May, it was stated that "the good old mine has not looked healthier for at least 23 years, perhaps for even a longer period". The figures presented were certainly impressive: Labour, £4,252 16s. 7d.; carriage £326 1s. 3d.; coal, £788 7s. 7d.; merchants, £1,068 13s.; sundries, £22 8s. 3d.; total, £6,458 6s. 9d. Credits: Tin, Botallack, £6,794 12s. 9d.; tin, Carnyorth, £2,239 17s. 9d.; total, £9,034 10s. 6d.; tin ready for market, £750; sundries, £63 5s. 4d.; total, £9,947 15s. 10d. Profit, £3,489 9s. 1d. Adding to this the previous credit balance of £748 18s. 2d. gave a final credit balance of £4,238 7s. 3d. A dividend of £16 per 200th share absorbed £3,200 of this, leaving £1,038 7s. 3d. to be carried forward. A month's salary, as a present, was offered to each agent and the Purser; whilst the Purser and the managing and principal underground captain, Mr. Henry Boyns, were given a £2 2s. monthly increase in salary. A reporter who attended "the usual hospitable dinner" on this occasion has left us a vivid description of the mine as it then was, in the Indian Summer of its prosperity: "There was the same busy scene of everyday toil, extending from the primeval workings of the old men . . . down over the steep sward and sudden cliff to the adits which pour their turbid waters into the stormy Atlantic. Comfortable changing house and outlying cumbrous chests of the old miners; thundering stamps, fed by small trucks on tramways, and leading to 'floors' where buddle, frame, and trunk, and catch-pits, kieves and hutches, held the tin which, under the hands of comely bal-girls and careful overlookers, changes from the grit of the stamps to the heavy mud for the smelter; zig-zag paths, giving glimpses of engine-houses perched on the cliffs above, and of engine-houses flung down on rocks beneath; a long and slender viaduct, from headland to headland, over a raging sea, and down which wooden perch runs the little skip that in eight minutes puts you half-a-mile from the coast and a quarter of a mile under the bed of the Atlantic; everywhere Man contending with the most stubborn elements, to win bread for himself and a profit for his employer." This observer was particularly attracted by "a kind of quadruple guillotine" standing near the carpenters' shop, and which was, in fact, an additional framework for the recently added steam stamps' heads to provide summer stamping power. [3]

At the August account (when the June report was presented) a dividend of £10 per share (£2,000) was declared, and a credit of £1,111 13s. 9d. carried forward. The working miners shared a little of the mine's prosperity, their average wages now being £3 5s. a month instead of £3, as formerly.

The account of November 17th showed that profits were a little lower (£1,074 2s. 6d.), a dividend of £6 per share being declared. Boscawen Shaft was sinking under the 240, the lode large, opening slight tin ground. At Carnyorth, they had communicated New Shaft to the 30 and opened up some tin ground.

Writing on December 18th 1869, Warrington Smyth noted that the undersea workings were proceeding with considerable vigour, considering that for the past two years the discoveries of ore made in these new deep excavations had been very small. "It is a singular fact that the place on which their Royal Highnesses, the Prince and Princess of Wales, stood, four years ago, in the 205 fathom level and broke a stone of ore proved to be but the narrow apex of a considerable body—some 30 fathoms in maximum length, from which most of the returns of the undersea workings have been made. But the whole of this ground has turned out poorer than expected; and though symptoms of tin and copper ores are not extinct, the bottom of the shaft, at 6 fathoms below the 240 fathom level, and the two or three ends driving forward, are all poor. A small trial is making higher up the shaft, at the 125; and a level on a South lode called Wheal Loor will in a few fathoms more pass under the sea line and afford further chance of undersea mineral." Wheal Cock had hardly ever been so destitute of orey appearance; and all that was doing under the sea was the advancing of the 135 fathom level seaward. Good profits were, nevertheless, being made from the large amount of tin being raised under the land—the exact converse of the position twenty or thirty years ago when all the riches were yielded by the copper ore under the sea.

11. Ladderway down to Wheal Cock Adit portal. The ladderway was 260 feet long from the cliff top to the adit portal platform. Men can be seen working on the collar of Wheal Cock Engine Shaft on cliff top. (1907)

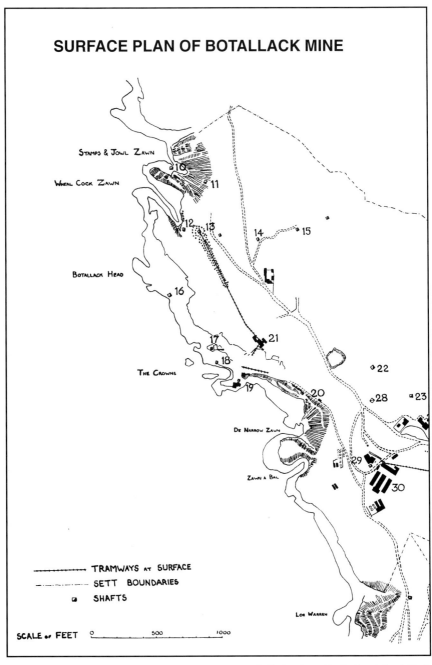

SURFACE PLAN OF BOTALLACK MINE

STAMPS & JOWL ZAWN
WHEAL COCK ZAWN
BOTALLACK HEAD
THE CROWNS
DE NARROW ZAWN
ZAWN A BAL
LOE WARREN

———————— TRAMWAYS AT SURFACE
—·—·—·—— SETT BOUNDARIES
▫ SHAFTS

SCALE OF FEET   0   500   1000

CARNYORTH SECTION: 1. Great Works Shaft   2. North Shaft   3. Rodds Shaft   4. Stock Shaft
5. Guide Shaft   6. Engine Shaft   7. Lobby Shaft   8. Pearces Shaft   9. Ninevah Shaft
WHEAL COCK SECTION: 10. Providence Shaft   11. Tolven Shaft   12. Wheal Cock Shaft
13. New Shaft (Skip Shaft)   14. Chicken Shaft   15. Wheal Hen Shaft
BOTALLACK SECTION: 16. Hard Shaft   17. Wheal Button   18. Boscawen Diaganol Shaft
19. Crowns Engine Shaft 20. Wheal Hazard Shaft 21. Crowns Whim 22. Cliffields Shaft

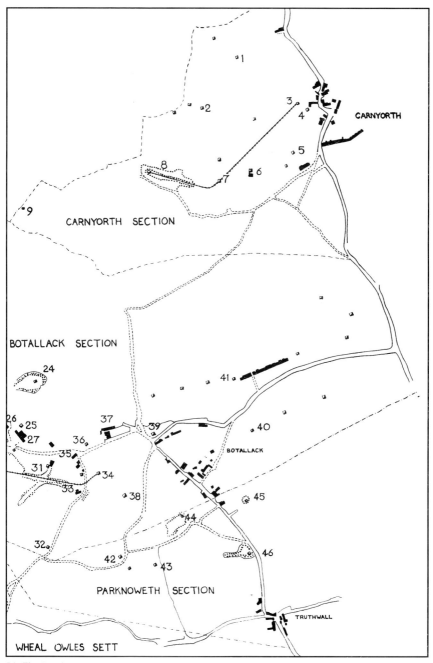

23. *Flat Road Shaft*   24. *Park Bunny Shaft*   25. *Old Engine Shaft*   26. *Account House*
27. *Whim and Saw Mill*   28. *Site of Allen Shaft*   29. *Narrow Shaft and Stamps*
30. *Dressing Floors*   31. *Botallack Engine Shaft*   32. *Chycornish Shaft*   33. *New Whim*
34. *Davy Shaft*   35. *Stores*   36. *Wheal Loor Shaft*   37. *Botallack House*   38. *Parknoweth Shaft*
39. *Ludgvan Shaft*   40. *Durloe Shaft* *(obliterated by new road)*
 41. *Shaft believed to be on Wheal Chase Lode*
PARKNOWETH SECTION: 42. *Parknoweth Engine Shaft*   43. *Flat Road Shaft*   44. *Buzza Shaft*
45. *Higher Buzza Street Shaft*   46. *Lane Shaft (filled in by road widening)*

14. Collaring Wheal Cock Engine Shaft in May 1907. The shaft was 11 feet in diameter. The top of the cliff ladder road can be seen in the background.

The December quarterly meeting (held in the account house on February 16th 1870), showed profits again lower, at £781, but a dividend of £1,000 (taken partly from the previous balance) was distributed. Reviewing the past year's achievements—truly Botallack's *annus mirabilis*—Capt. Henry Boyns gave the total credits as £37,055 10s. 7d.; profits, £7,617 18s. 8d.; ground broken, 5,846¹/₃ fathoms, or 6¹/₂ miles; and tinstuff broken, 207,041 sacks, or 22,846 tons, equal to about 4 tons to the fathom. From a portion of this stuff (190,464 sacks) 494¹/₄ tons of tin and 33 tons of copper was obtained. The average price of tin for the first three quarters was £75 1s., and for the fourth £66 2s. Stamping cost was 13s. 2d. per 100 sacks, against 32s. twenty years ago. There were 14 powerful steam engines at work, whilst the tin-dressing floors were equal in completeness to any in Cornwall—with 24 round buddles, and 13 round rotary frames. Formerly 112 girls had been employed on the floors, but since the introduction of the buddles their number was reduced to 44. Altogether, about 600 were employed at Botallack.[4]

Around the end of January 1870, a new lode was discovered at the junction of the Carnyorth and Wheal Cock boundaries, in a cross-cut W. at the 64 fathom level. In the S. wall it was 18 inches wide, containing good tinstuff, and had a very promising appearance. It lay about 13 fathoms S. of the main lode, and appeared to have a more westerly course than either the Nogger or Wheal Hen. Two new cross-cuts were at once pushed on towards the same object at the 42 and 88 fathom levels on the same cross-course. Further good news came in March, when an improvement was announced in the 132 fathom level W. at Wheal Cock.

A melancholy interest attaches to the quarterly meeting held on May 18, as it was the last attended by Stephen Harvey James, who had for so many years directed the affairs of this great mine. It is pleasing to record that Botallack, at that time, appeared to be riding the crest of a wave of renewed prosperity; Stephen James was thus spared the bitterness of the dark years of decline that lay in store for his successors. At this meeting, the agents, in addition to reporting on the previous discoveries, announced another, even more noteworthy, at the very bottom of the Boscawen Shaft, then sunk 18 fathoms diagonally under the 240. Here a tin lode had been intersected as large as "the whole bigness of the shaft". It was believed that one of the Wheal Cock lodes had fallen in at this point, and formed a junction with the Great Crowns lode; should this prove the case it might lead to a very rich discovery. Previously, this part had yielded rich copper ore to an enormous extent, giving £24,000 in dividends in a single year. The 240 had been driving W. and N., and a winze sinking to communicate the shaft had cut the lode just a few feet above the junction of shaft and winze. It was valued, at first, at a ton of tin per fathom, but this estimate had later to be slightly reduced.

The statistical details for this quarter were: Wages, £4,834 11s. 8d.; merchants, £933 4s. 9d.; tin credited last account, £2,700; total, £9,952 11s. 6,389 tons of stuff had been crushed, yielding 118 tons of tin. Copper ore was sold to the value of £176 19s. 4d.; 120 tons of Botallack tin, less dues £8,982 6s. 10d.; 38¼ tons of Carnyorth tin, less dues, £2,733 12s. 11d.; sundry credits, £69—£11,961 19s. 1d. The profit was £2,009 8s. 1d., which added to a previous balance, showed a total favourable balance of £2,776 4s. 9d. From this, a dividend of £10 per 200th share was declared.

At this meeting, Mr. James acknowledged the toast of "The health of the purser"; but only a fortnight later his death was announced. He had filled the position for nearly 35 years, and "in this office had been the means of employing thousands of persons, the channel through which splendid dividends passed to fortunate shareholders, and the representative of employers and employed to the many distinguished visitors to the picturesque scene of his labours ... Hundreds of friends will mourn the loss of one whose firmness, decision and energy made him an excellent man of business, and who united with these solid qualities a kindness and freshness of heart which caused him to be respected alike by old and young". James was then aged 75. One of his three sons—Stephen Harvey James, jun.—had assisted his father for some time in the management of the mine; another, Joseph, died abroad; and John, the third, was a London surgeon.

The *Mining Journal* of September 3rd reported a recent discovery of bismuth in the deepest part of the Crown's lode, worth 12s. to 14s. per lb. when smelted. Most of it was rich stuff, though only a little bunch. Carne had recorded in 1822 the finding of native bismuth in two of the tin and copper lodes at Botallack; but the best specimens for the mineralogist's cabinet had already ceased, only inferior ones then being discovered. The present specimens agreed with his description of the auriferous sulphuret of bismuth. "The miners of half a century ago, as a few weeks since, ascertained the presence of the metal by thrusting the mineral into an ordinary fire, when it oozed out in small globules."

This month also saw the completion of the tram road to the bottom of the Diagonal Shaft. The 250 level—which proved to be the lowest ever driven in the Crowns—was working for tin and copper. In Higher Mine, the skip road was complete to the 60 fathom level, where they were laying a tram road. The 100 S. on Guide in Wheal Hazard was rising against a winze under the 65, opening fair tin ground, whilst the 100 S. on Bal lode was producing a little tin and copper. At Wheal Cock, the 112 W. on Wheal Hen was opening tin ground, as also were the 85 and 70 E. In Carnyorth, the 88 and 64 W. on New Lode were opening paying tin ground, whilst in the 88 cross-cut a lode thought to be Wheal Hen had been intersected. The adit end E. on the curiously named New Wynstock or Winnowing Stock lode was yielding a little tin. The agents further announced that the New Steam Whim would soon be in order. A large quantity of broken tinstuff was awaiting the increasing stamping power it would provide.

The November account revealed a profit of £1,003 2s., a £5 dividend being distributed. Capt. Henry Boyns gave an interesting account to the shareholders of the summer's drought at the mine. The deep sea adit level at Higher Botallack, which was 45 fathoms from surface and drained a large part of the workings, had been, until about November 6th, almost dry, this condition having lasted there for several months. By contrast, during the rainy winter season he had often witnessed a river rushing through it. At Wheal Cock, where the workings reached 170 fathoms below sea level and a quarter of a mile in length the water pumped from underground did not exceed 12 gallons per minute. At Higher Mine, 205 fathoms deep and half a mile long, the water raised from below deep adit did not exceed 80 gallons per minute. At the Crowns, 250 fathoms below sea level and two-thirds of a mile long (including half a mile under the sea) the quantity amounted to no more than 190 gallons per minute. During this four months' period they had often been at their wits' ends to obtain sufficient water to supply the steam stamps, floors and round buddles. In the Nancherrow Valley, where all their water stamps were situated, the wheels had been almost idle for months— one large water stamps of 24 heads not having stamped a single sack of tinstuff for half a year.

Writing on December 3rd, Warrington Smyth stated that during the past year, Botallack had continued to employ a number of men at the Crowns, but had lost money upon it, although the concern as a whole, from the large production of tin inland, had given profits. "The recent death of the purser, Mr. James, who was identified with all the best history of the mine, may, I fear, be a severe blow, for already I have heard at the mine doubts expressed as to the prospects in depth which were scarcely allowed to be mooted under his spirited regime." When Smyth descended the Diagonal Shaft there were temporarily 5 fathoms of water at the bottom, but a promising little vein of tin ore had been cut there. The 240 level had been opened for 30 fathoms in length N. of the shaft, and presented the small pyritous character of the Wheal Cock lode rather than that of the Crown. "In fact with depth the copper ore has for the present entirely vanished, and none whatever has been sold or returned for some months past." Drivings at the 200 and 225 fathom levels had only confirmed this deterioration in copper ore, not counterbalanced by a few bunches of tin. However, a further trial was about to commence under sea in a neighbouring lode called Wheal Loor, one of the Botallack land lodes. It had been driven on at 65 fathoms under adit for 136 fathoms from Narrow Shaft to near the sea line without yielding any useful mineral, but now offered a more favourable appearance, inducing further researches North Westwards. He had suggested to the agents the desirability of pushing forward a cross-cut at the 115 fathom level to cut this lode. At Wheal Cock only the 112 and 135 were driving W., both with some tin ore but hardly worth following

Stephen Harvey James was succeeded as purser by his son of the same name. The latter is first mentioned as holding that office in a report of the February account for 1871, where it was stated he had "so far recovered from his recent accident as to be present, but the chair was occupied by Mr. N. B. Downing, ex-mayor of Penzance". The figures presented showed that a good price was still being obtained for tin, varying from £72 10s. to £85 10s. but the profit amounted to only £800 7s. 4d. However, a dividend of £1,000 was declared, partly derived from reserves. The agents reported they were taking away tin ground over the 250 in the Crowns, whilst the 240 driving N. was again producing a little copper. At Wheal Hazard, a cross-cut at the 85 was driving towards South Wheal Cock. In the Carnyorth section, Rodd's Shaft had been sunk 5 fathoms under adit, but was suspended on account of water. The adit end on Winnowing Stock lode was yielding a little tin. The new Steam Whim was working, enabling the steam stamps to be employed full time, but dressing of the stuff had been impeded by frost. During the quarter no less than 1,723 fathoms 3 feet 3 inches of ground had been opened; whilst for the year 1870 the total amounted to seven and one-sixth miles, six feet high, yielding 236,389 sacks of tinstuff. £34,237 17s. 11d. was earned, £29,565 3s. 3d. spent; leaving a profit of £4,672 17s. 8d.

In May, it was announced that Botallack's tin sales for the quarter would be about 147 tons, but owing to the falling standard for that metal, the amount received for it would be at least £600 less than if sold during the previous quarter. However, a discovery of grey copper ore had advanced the price of the shares from £230 to £250. In their quarterly report, the agents mentioned two pitches working for tin and copper over the 240, and 4 pitches over the 180, in the Crowns, at tributes from 10s.—15s. in the £. In Higher Mine, a winze was sinking under the 80 N. to communicate Wheal Hazard. At Wheal Hazard itself, they had cut South Wheal Cock lode in the cross-cut at the 85 E., where it looked well for copper ore. This was the same lode that produced copper in the Crowns. At Carnyorth, they had a winze over the 64 S. and another under the 42 to ventilate levels on New Lode.

Profits were up again in August to £1,488 10s. 9d., a dividend of £6 being distributed. There were 41 pitches working on tut and 2 on tribute at Carnyorth; at the Crowns, 3 pitches working on tribute over the 180; at Higher Mine, 61 pitches on tut; and at Wheal Cock, 13 pitches on tut. The new lode recently intersected at Wheal Hazard had opened several fathoms of copper ground.

In an interesting article on Botallack, published on September 16th, the *Mining Journal* noted that there were very few "foreigners" among its shareholders, the 200 shares into which the mine was divided being held by only 84 adventurers, nearly all of whom were resident in the locality. Three-quarters of the mine were held by the same families who had started the concern in 1836. About 700 hands were employed, 400 of these underground. The earnings of the latter averaged £3 5s. per month, but a large number earned £4 and upwards. There were 156 heads of stamps, of which 106 were worked by steam and 48 by water. Fourteen steam engines were used for pumping, drawing and stamping but the size of these was much smaller than those in the Redruth or Camborne districts, the largest draught-engine on the mine being only a 36-inch.

At the next shareholders' meeting, held on November 15th, the quarter's receipts were announced as £8,668 3s. 4d., and expenditure as £8,155 3s. 9d., giving a profit of £512 19s. 7d. The costs included £100 for a patent pulveriser. The agents reported that the 135 S. in the Crowns had been cleared 50 fathoms, and the men were now engaged in laying tramroad. They were also clearing the 115 S. for the purpose of driving a cross-cut in the western wall. No mention was made of the deeper workings in this section. At Higher Mine the 205 and 90 N. were still driving and opening good tin ground. They daily expected to communicate with Wheal Hazard. At Chycornish, a cross-cut driving at the 50 was expected to cut the Bussa lode in a few more fathoms. The 100 S. on Bal lode in Wheal Hazard was driving, ground very hard with a good vein of copper in the end, but being in granite they feared for its permanence. The ends N. and S. of cross-cut at the 85 on South Wheal Cock lode were still producing a small quantity of copper; since cutting this lode about six months ago, 16 fathoms had been opened on it. They hoped that this lode, on leaving the cross-course, would have improved, but so far there was nothing to value, though its appearance was promising. In Carnyorth, the 30 on Great Work Guide was driving towards Rodd's lode. The quality of tinstuff in the mine had fallen off during the quarter. The committee, in expressing regret at the smaller dividend (£2 10s.) asserted that they had not been able to return some partially dressed tin. They also reminded the adventurers that the new machine, erected for grinding roughs, had only just begun working, and the results anticipated from it had consequently not been realised.

This pulveriser appears to have given the mine a great deal of trouble; and on December 6th it was announced that a special meeting of the adventurers was to be held the following week on "a question of patented machinery and the claims of the patentees". Its outcome has not been traced. On December 13th, however, it was announced that Capt. Frank Bennetts, of Ding Dong, would succeed Capt. John Boyns, who had resigned.[5]

In his December report, Warrington Smyth announced that the deeper works below the 180 fathom level had been given up as offering no prospect of success, and all exploratory work abandoned save at the 115 fathom level where they were preparing to open a cross-cut southward to intersect the Spar lode which had been driven upon from other land-workings to a few yards beyond the cliff and was looking moderately well for tin. More activity prevailed at Wheal Cock, where he examined the 100, 112 and 135 fathom levels, all having small lodes but with a fair proportion of tin. The land workings, though not rich, were yielding a large amount of mineral, from the extensive number of lodes which were in work.

A singular accident occurred on January 5th 1872, when a newly greased tram-waggon was set in motion by the wind's violence above the Crowns, and ran down a steep incline and smashed into a small shed, injuring three bal-maids within, one seriously. Trouble of another kind occurred in February. A dispute broke out between the men and management on the question of the four weeks' month, which was then causing much controversy in Cornish mining.[6] The miners demanded the abolition of the old five weeks month; and the management committee, meeting at Penzance, decided to grant this, on condition that the men abandoned their traditional "Mazed Monday" holiday. The management also offered to pay at mid-day on Friday, so enabling the miner's wife to go to market and the miner to prepare his tools and have a little relaxation before resuming work on Monday morning. On Friday March 1st (a pay and setting day) four members of the committee met the men at the mine to state their views on the dispute. Pay at Botallack took place in a front room of the account house, where the money—on this occasion about £2,000—was counted out for each pare of miners, or for a single hand, as the case might be. Setting was transacted from the window of a back apartment; and those who had finished bargaining for their pitches, went round to the pay table. Some hundreds of men being assembled, Mr. James read them the committee's resolutions. The taking that day would be from March 1st to the 29th, which was Good Friday. The men applauded his speech and the tribute pitches and tutwork bargains were then submitted. Many of these were arranged so as to give the miners work for three and two months. Most were promptly taken, and the occasion passed off without any unpleasant incident. One of the committee said in a speech that "Fridays pays, and the abolition of Mazed Mondays would be in their [the men's] interests —must benefit them morally, must benefit their families, must benefit their prospects in life, and must tend to make them better men in every sense of the word". All very true, no doubt; but many must have regretted the passing of another pleasant, if somewhat disreputable, old custom.[7]

It was reported in March that Dingey's Pulveriser, operated by steam from the 64 heads stamps' engine had returned eight tons of tin the last quarter. The May account disclosed a profit of £1,217 17s. 3d., and the 101st dividend was declared at £6 a share. Wheal Hazard Shaft had been sunk ten fathoms, from the 100 to the 110 and turned out 4 tons of tin. This shaft was to be fitted with a skip and connected to the stamps by a tram—"an expensive but needful job". There were 37 tutwork and 7 tribute pitches for tin in Higher Mine. The August profit amounted to £1,004 2s. 9d., but otherwise the account was not a very cheerful one: "Subject only to the sudden and gratifying discoveries of copper and tin which the history of Botallack has so often disclosed, the prospects are not quite so bright as they were. The copper lode in the Crowns changed into tin; Wheal Hazard will take £1,500 in the sinking of a shaft, before much tin ground can be taken away; other parts of the mine are poor; and the prices of materials, but, more particularly, the scarcity of men, tell against the mine. The agents hold out little hope of a dividend next quarter, unless something favourable occurs in the meantime."

This gloomy prediction was more than fulfilled, for in November a loss of £708 was announced. Copper had been credited at £301 and tin at £6,529. In the Crowns, the end N. of winze under the 180 N. was producing a little tin, whilst the 165 S. from Wheal Button was driving. The 135 S. had holed to old workings. In Wheal Hazard, the shaft had been cut down and double skip road fixed to shallow adit. A tram road had also been laid from the top of the cliff to Steam Stamps (175 fathoms) and the men were fixing a skip road from shallow adit to the cliff top. It was estimated that cross-cuts driving in Higher Mine at adit and the 60 towards Wheal Chase would take six months to cut the lode. In Wheal Cock they were preparing an air machine to ventilate adit level preparatory to driving.

Writing in December, Smyth stated he had visited the St. Just mines in late October and early November, and found that nearly all had been very unsuccessful that year. "The active emigration of the miners and the somewhat higher rate of wages seem to have counterbalanced the undoubtedly good price of tin in the market; and the lodes have exhibited an unexpected degree of poverty." At Botallack, some favourable appearances for tin in the Spar lode in the 65 fathom level had ceased, and from scarcity of men the place had been left idle. It was proposed to communicate the 165 level under the sea with the workings of the 135 level at Wheal Cock, which was a separate mine, and thus economise the pumping power as well as improve the ventilation of both divisions. No real exploratory work was going forward in the Crowns; but in Wheal Cock the 100 fathom level was driving Westward in a tin bearing lode about one foot wide, and the 112 and 135 fathom levels had communicated works advancing in ground which assured some moderate returns of tin. "On the whole, however, I cannot but regard the situation of the mine as precarious for the extensive workings under the land, though they have yielded pretty largely up to the present time, are barely able to show a margin of profit."

Truly, the tide had turned, and was now strongly on the ebb.

1 MS., per Miss D. R. Chirgwin, St. Just.
2 Quoted by *Mining Journal*, December 7th 1867.
3 *Comish Telegraph*, May 26th 1869.
4 *Cornish Telegraph*, January 5th and February 23rd 1870.
5 *Cumish Telegraph*, December 6th and 13th 18/1.
6 For a detailed treatment of the "five weeks' month" question, and the disputes arising from it, see *D. B. Barton's History of Tin Mining and Smelting in Comwall*, p. 148.
7 *Comish Telegraph*, March 6th 1872.

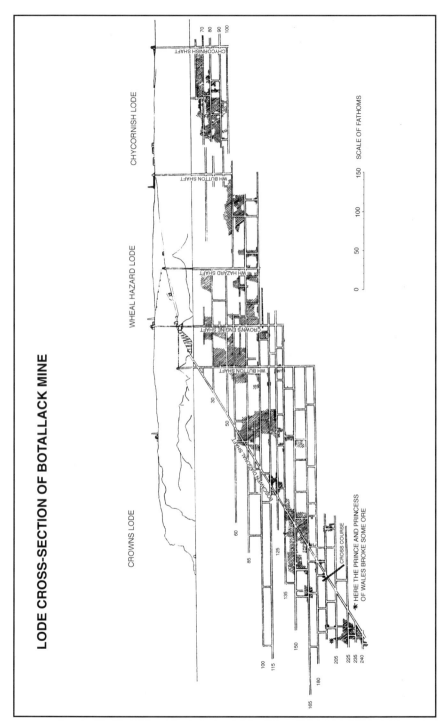

LODE CROSS-SECTION OF BOTALLACK MINE

Chapter Five:
Hopes and Disappointments

The loss shown at the account in February 1873, was £802 2s., this being largely accounted for by the rising price of coal. In the corresponding quarter of 1872, 1,231 tons of coal had been burnt, at a cost of £762; but for this quarter 1,117 tons cost no less than £1,321. The sinking of Wheal Hazard Shaft had also been an expensive operation, although this was now completed, and should lead to the opening up of fresh tin ground. A skip road had been laid in this shaft from the cliff top to the bottom of the mine, and the drawing engine put in good order. It was intended to sink still lower eventually and drive N. and S. at 115 fathoms.

At the following account held on May 21, the purser stated that 106 tons of tin had been sold at an average price of £83 2s. 6d. per ton, for £8,804 16s. 3d. In the corresponding quarter of 1872 the average price had been £91 5s. a ton, and the price of coal had been 12s. 11d. a ton, compared with 20s. 10d. now. This had made a difference of £1,400 between the two quarters: in addition, labour, iron, timber and materials were all dearer. Mr. James therefore maintained that, although a profit of only £47 had been achieved, the mine was in a better condition than a year before. The agents reported favourably on the new system of Friday "pays" and Monday "viewing" days. It was resolved that in future quarterly accounts should be held alternately on the mine and at Penzance.

The August meeting, held at Penzance, proved to be one of the most unfavourable presented for many years. Costs for the three months were £8,191, 79 tons of tin having been sold at prices ranging from £83 at the commencement of the quarter to £76 at its conclusion. The loss was £2,419, though against this unsold tin and copper was estimated to be worth £1,000. The shareholders resolved to petition Lord Falmouth and the other lords for a remission of dues, and also to convene a special meeting to make a call. However, several levels throughout the mine were looking better, and prospects were thought to be more favourable. In the Crowns, the winze under 180 S. on branch W. of Guide was producing tin. Wheal Hazard Shaft had recommenced sinking under the 115, the 115 N. producing low quality tin, the 115 S. being poor. The 180 W. in Higher Mine was producing stones of tin, but the 150 E. had proved a disappointment, the ground being very hard and poor, in marked contrast to that over the 130. A cross-cut at the 60 had cut a lode, not yet proved to be Wheal Chase. In Wheal Cock, skip road had been completed to the 50 below adit, the shaft cut down to the 60, stone collar completed, and shaft tackle sufficiently high erected to tram stuff to the stamps. New Shaft was being put down with all speed in Carnyorth.

"The diminution in the returns of tin was caused by a falling off in quantity and quality of tinstuff in Higher Mine, and a short supply of water at the stamps. We estimate the value of tin and copper undressed at surface at £100."

The loss at the November account amounted to £821 12s. 11d. making a total debit of £2,860; a call of £5 was made. Copper featured in the returns, 52 tons 13 cwt. realising (less dues) £762 14s. 11d. 1,053 tons of coal had been burnt at a cost of £1,030 17s. At Higher Mine, Wheal Chase lode had been intersected in the cross cut. At Carnyorth, Nineveh Shaft was being prepared for working the western ground. Rodd's Shaft was sunk to the 30 and communicated to a cross-cut driven from Engine Shaft.

Affairs took on a much grimmer aspect at the account held on February 25th 1874, when the three months' loss came to £2,773 8s. 9d., making a total debit balance of £4,665 15s. 8d. Mr. T. S. Bolitho proposed that a call of £2 be made, which was carried. It was also resolved that a renewed application be sent to the lords for a relinquishment of dues, Lord Falmouth having received over £30,000 in dues from Botallack. The committee recommended that the whole of the Crowns and Wheal Hazard should be at once suspended and this was unanimously approved by the shareholders, as those extensive sections could not be carried on except at a considerable monthly loss. The agents were also asked to submit a special report on the prospects of Higher Mine at an extraordinary meeting to be held in a month's time, when a decision would be taken regarding its further working or suspension. Mr. James remarked they had received £7 10s. a ton less for their tin this quarter than last. The price now obtaining was £60 per ton, whilst he had sold the same quality in April 1872, for £95 per ton. Mr. F. Boase, Mayor of Penzance, commented: "As far as the working miners are concerned, I do not think they are paid too high wages, but … I consider the adventurers should get much more work done for the money … In order to meet the times a reduction should be made on all wages and salaries, beginning from the purser and agents down to the lowest of their working staff." Another considerable shareholder endorsed this view, saying he believed they did not get as much work done for 20s. as they did ten years ago for 10s.

Because of the decision taken at this meeting to close certain sections of Botallack, the agents' report then presented (for October-December 1873) was the last ever produced covering the whole of this large mine, and is given here in full, as a curiosity:

Crowns. Winze under 180 S. of Boscawen Shaft communicated to 190, both ends poor. Tin gone through in the winze does not continue.

Wheal Hazzard. Shaft sunk 13 fathoms under 115, lode unproductive. 115 N. and S. on Guide are poor. 151 S. on what we thought was Wheal Hazzard lode is unsatisfactory. Sunk Winze under 115 N., lode poor. Winze sunk under 100 S. holed to 115 and produced low quality tin stuff. Have opened on a vein at 65 W. of Guide, not produced anything to pay.

Higher Mine. 205 N. producing good stones tinstuff 205 E. on Park Bunney driving towards Bal lode, which has not been seen under 170. 180 E. and W. on Wheal Loor poor, former suspended. 60 W. on Wheal Chase poor. Winze sinking under adit to ventilate this and 60. 50 E. on Bussa in paying tin ground. Winze under 50 E. in paying ground.

Wheal Cock. 100 S. producing tin and promising. 90 S. is in paying tin ground. 85 S. producing tin and copper. New Shaft is cut down and nearly completed to 100.

Carnyorth. 135, 124, 112 and 100 E. of Engine Shaft, producing little tin. Rising over 135 W. against Pearce's Shaft, which is sinking under 100, ground producing little tin. New lode very productive in 84 and 64 levels. Nineveh Shaft being continued, 30 E. and W. doing fairly well. Skip Road in Rodd's Shaft completed to 30. Now laying tram road in this and the 30 on Guide to facilitate working of Rodd's and Winnowing Stock lodes. Adit E. on Rodd's and W. on Stock lodes are poor.

The agents themselves made the following recommendation: "In present state of tin market and high price of labor and materials we cannot speak of our openings as paying, though in Carnyorth and Wheal Cock parts of the mine, they are up to what they have been. Recommend abandoning Crowns … and suspending operations in Wheal Hazzard until 205 N. from Higher Mine has been driven under the Wheal Hazzard Shaft."

An old adage has it that "troubles never come singly"; and this must have seemed to be confirmed when the large fly wheel of the stamps' engine broke on February 24th 1874, the cost of its repair being considerable. At their adjourned meeting at the Western Hotel, Penzance, on March 20, the adventurers decided, after a long discussion, to keep the water out of Higher Mine, to stope no ground (but take away what was broken), and to continue the 205 N. and the 205 cross-cut E.

These measures proved only a partial remedy, the May account showing a still heavy loss of £1,298 9s. 1d. A call of £7 a share was made. 97$^{1}/_{2}$ tons of tin had been sold at an average price of £53 6s. a ton—£10 under the preceding quarter and £30 under the corresponding quarter of 1873. Capts. F. Bennetts, F. Oats and H. Hosking reported that in Higher Mine 54 men and boys were breaking tin. In Wheal Cock the New Shaft was cut down and skip road nearly completed to the 112. In Carnyorth the lode in Pearce's Shaft was large and producing tin throughout. "During the past quarter the very low price of tin has compelled us to reduce the number of men employed in opening out the mine." After dinner, Mr. N. B. Downing thanked both purser and agents for the efforts they had made to economise in every way consistent with the proper development of the mine. Replying, Mr. James expressed his belief that the worst was over

His optimism—in a short term view, at least—was justified for the August meeting disclosed a quarterly profit of £383 19s. This result, however, was achieved by enforcing the most savage economy measures; overall expenses had been reduced by nearly 50 per cent, and labour by about half that. Despite this cut in wages, the Purser stated that "the men worked better than before". No doubt they had to, in order to get anything like a living wage. As a result they had raised considerably more tin than anticipated, their efforts being aided by a general improvement in the ground. A settlement was announced in the dispute with Wheal Owles over the latter's encroachment into Botallack sett. Wheal Owles had paid dues on the tin they had removed, and a sum of £127 would complete the transaction. The agents reported the 205 N. in Higher Mine had been driving and in the last fathom had produced some good stones of tin. A winze was sinking under this level in paying tin ground. Despite the economy measures, development work was still being actively undertaken; and 66 tutmen were engaged in prosecuting ends and opening up the mine.[1]

On September 17th, valuable lodes of copper were announced as having been cut both in Wheal Cock and Wheal Hazard. The *Cornish Telegraph's* correspondent was shown a specimen of very rich grey copper cut from a point where the lode was 2 feet wide and worth £20 per fathom. There was further good news at the November account, when the quarterly profit amounted to £491, and the shareholders were promised—on the basis of the agents' report—"something like the dividends of the good old times" in the not too distant future.

This report stated that the 205 N. in Higher Mine, producing a little tin, would eventually drain the ground through which Wheal Hazard Shaft—intended as a sump shaft for working tin ground in the bottom of the level—must be sunk. The driving of the cross-cut at the 110 in the E. wall to cut Wheal Chase and other lodes had been resumed; if anything productive was found, Davy's Skip Shaft would be used for discharging. In Wheal Cock, New Shaft from the 112 had been communicated to the 124. The cross-cut at the 112 W. had been holed to a winze under the 100, and had proved the lode there to be another lode N. of the Tolven and Wheal Hen lodes. The ends E. and W. of cross-cut appeared most promising. A winze under the adit E. had been sunk 8 fathoms, and would soon communicate with the 64 W. at Carnyorth. At Carnyorth itself, Pearce's Shaft had been communicated to the rise over the 135, whilst Nineveh and Rodd's Shafts were both still sinking.

During that winter the St. Just mines were much troubled by the effects of excessive rains. On January 19th 1875, both Botallack and St. Just Amalgamated lost the lower lifts of their pumps. Botallack was stated to be "manfully fighting the antagonist, and at the Carnyorth part of this large concern the engines and the floods are struggling for the mastery inch by inch". Speaking at a Wheal Owles account a few days earlier, Richard Boyns (Purser) stated that at the Buzza part of that mine they were, and had been for some time, pumping a large portion of Botallack water, owing to the running in of Chycornish part of Botallack, and were threatened to be flooded at any moment from that quarter. It was therefore resolved that a committee be appointed to negotiate regarding the flow of water from Botallack into the Buzza, to settle the encroachment "unwittingly made by Wheal Owles on Botallack, and to determine on the further prosection of the Buzza otherwise"[2]

The February account saw Botallack just meeting cost, with a profit of £218. May showed a slight improvement, the favourable balance then being £603 1s. 4d. An interesting feature of the account was the sum of £19 1s. credited for arsenic, showing that the management were beginning to appreciate the value of this hitherto neglected product.[3] At Higher Mine preparations were being made to sink Engine Shaft below the 205. The 85 E. on Tolven in Wheal Cock had greatly improved, the lode, 18 inches wide, consisting of arsenic and tin. In Carnyorth, Pearce's Shaft skip road was being completed to the 135. "We are erecting Kilns, Flues, &c., to burn our Arsenical Stuff, and hope soon to make considerable returns from same."

Profit on the August quarter amounted to £70 4s. 5d. It was resolved to hold all future meetings on the mine. Capts. Francis Bennetts and John Hallo reported that in Higher Mine the 80 N. on Corpus Christi had been cleared to the end, which was producing a little tin and copper. There were about 200 fathoms between this and the 100 S. at Wheal Cock, and this was considered to be a very promising piece of unexplored ground. The 100 S. at Wheal Cock had itself intersected an E.-W. lode which was yielding tin and copper. The adit E. had been communicated to Carnyorth. By this time, the Botallack sett had been slightly increased in area. In May, the Botallack and Wheal Owles mine committees met and arranged to transfer a portion of Truthwall sett to Botallack adventurers for a sum of £300. This enabled Botallack to continue working a lode into the N.E. part of Wheal Owles ground.

The *Cornish Telegraph* (September 1st) carried an interesting account of the new arsenic works at Botallack: "Arsenic has much improved in value of late. Botallack has no end of arsenic on the surface and underground. Hitherto this produce was unprofitable. Now that £6 10s. a ton can be obtained for it, the old burrows and reserves are being hunted, and great piles of the gleaming stones are seen at surface, awaiting the construction of a burning house. Lucrezia Borgia

77

would see something to admire on Botallack beyond the stately cliffs and ever-rolling main. Half-a-dozen circular kilns, 3 feet in diameter, are being built within a few yards of where an unlucky step backwards would send the heedless one hurtling down the jagged rocks and into the foaming Atlantic. A cross-flue leads inland to the main flues—a series of arched chambers, 72 in number, with orifices in their connecting walls, which give the fumes from the scorching mundic and arsenic a distance of 374 yards to traverse, whereon to deposit the white and deadly crystals of commerce. Then a stack, 112 feet high, conducts the smoke, and whatever undeposited arsenic it contains, to the upper air. If this article holds its price Botallack will have a case of arsenical dividend."

Mr. James announced a profit of £400 at the November account. Wheal Cock Skip Shaft had been completed to the 135, whilst at Carnyorth Rodd's Shaft was sinking under the 40 for a fork. Smyth, summarising progress during 1875 (in his report of January 13th 1876) stated that the mine had increased its returns, but the chief undersea part, the Crowns, was still full of water. However, the considerable improvement in the submarine part of Wheal Cock seemed likely to lead to a resumption of the Crowns during 876—a hope which, in fact, was not realised.

Affairs showed a less favourable aspect at the February account for 1876, when a quarter's loss of £582 4s. 7d. was recorded. At Carnyorth, they had opened a considerable quantity of ground which, at the current low price of tin, could not be worked at a profit, and the agents consequently recommended its suspension. The adventurers, "though with considerable reluctance", adopted this report, and the whole of the Carnyorth part of the enterprise was therefore abandoned until the advent of better times. A total of 87 men and boys would be thrown out of work if employment could not be found for them in other parts of the mine; it was feared that a large number could not be re-absorbed, however. The gloom of the occasion was emphasised by the fact that barely one half of the number which normally surrounded the hospitable board partook of the account dinner. At its conclusion, Mr. James told his fellow shareholders that since they had last met—never in the same space of time, and with an equal number of hands, had they opened up so many fathoms of levels and winzes. Despite this, they had suffered a reverse, which Capt. Frank Bennetts accounted for by the fact that various parts of the mine had fallen off in productivity, and the further drop in the price of tin. As to the future, they had not a large stock of mineral in sight, but present appearances were good. Arsenic and copper would continue to assist them, but they must look mainly to the yield of tin and the price for that mineral. The deepest part of the mine now working was 150 fathoms below adit. The three ends opening into Truthwall had materially helped them to hold their own and relieve the mine of water. Without this means of drainage they would have been half drowned. Though he gave no details, this renewed flooding appears to have taken place during the previous November, when both Botallack and Wheal

Owles had greatly suffered. Captains and men were watching and working both night and day, and eventually the inrush was mastered. Concerning their new arsenic works, Mr. James remarked that it made ground pay that would hardly be remunerative for copper alone. This was particularly the case in the shallower parts of Wheal Cock and the upper portion of the mine.

The decision to close Carnyorth was not implemented till May 12th. The event was described in a Penzance newspaper as a "great calamity . . . Several men were previously out of work in the parish, and now there are 60 or 70 men discharged; unless there is a yet further exodus of our miners, many will have to apply for parochial relief ". The miners alleged there were several productive parts there which were sure to be worked again soon, and that therefore to suspend operations was simply to stock tin underground instead of at surface, whilst the work could never be done more cheaply than now. Future events were to justify these opinions.

At the account on May 16th a further loss of £705 was announced. This figure did not include a sum of £403 paid to Wheal Owles for the portion of the Truthwall sett. Copper ore sales totalled £1,184, and arsenic £100; whilst tin dressed and ready for sale was credited at £3,780. In Higher Mine they were working a little deeper again, the 180 E. on Wheal Loor producing tin of low quality. At Wheal Cock, Skip Shaft was sunk 4 fathoms under the 135 for a plot, which was being secured. The 85 on Tolven was still poor; the end was proving the ground on this lode between Wheal Cock and Carnyorth. In Carnyorth, now idle, the water was being kept to the 100 fathoms level.

The agents' report for April to June shows only two parts of the sett working—Higher Mine and Wheal Cock—but in the following quarter operations at Carnyorth were resumed, albeit on a restricted scale. No explanation for this resumption can be traced in any reports of the time; the price of tin can hardly have been an inducement, as it only averaged around £43 a ton. However, the general appearance of the mine had improved, and the adventurers may consequently have decided to make a further trial at Carnyorth. The initial results were certainly favourable, as in the 100 E. and W. on New Lode they were opening good tin ground, five men being employed thereon, with 33 others stoping ground on tribute. At Higher Mine, 22 men and 3 boys were opening ground, and 79 men and 7 boys stoping on tut and tribute. Wheal Cock Skip Shaft was 145 fathoms deep, the ground favourable and producing payable stuff. A winze under the 135 W. was opening paying ground for copper. The New Lode from Carnyorth was cut here between 40-50 fathoms below the deepest level driven at that sett. Twentythree men and 9 boys were opening ground, and 52 men and 7 boys stoping on tut and tribute. The November account reflected the generally improved position, a profit of £27 12s. 2d. being achieved. This, and calls totalling £511 17s. 6d., had lessened the heavy debit balance of £3,108 13s.

at the previous account to £2,569 3s. 4d., carried forward. Debit items included £46 8s. to Messrs. Rodd & Cornish for Carnyorth sett—presumably expenses connected with its re-granting. Carnyorth had produced 13 tons 13 cwt. of tin, realising £560 15s.

On December 21st, Warrington Smyth noted that Botallack, so far from removing any of its engines, had been occupied at heavy expense in completing a new shaft at Wheal Cock to facilitate the deeper workings, much of which would probably be beneath the sea. Some favourable copper appearances had been opened at the 100 and 112 fathom levels, but just inshore of the sealine. At the abandoned Crowns, the water had filled all the deeper levels.

The February 1877 account, showed the mine still holding its own, with a profit of £202. In Higher Mine, the 90 S. on Corpus Christi and 60 E. on Wheal Loor were being cleared preparatory to driving. Wheal Cock Skip Shaft had been sunk to the 150, and the men were cutting a skip plot at the 135. The 150 E. was driving and producing a little tin. In the 125 E. they had discovered the Corpus Christi lode, on which they were driving and rising; the lode had a promising appearance and was yielding both tin and copper. In Carnyorth, the 100 E. and W. on New Lode were opening good tin ground. A winze sinking under the 64 W. on Nogger and the 40 and 30 W. driving W. on Rodd's lode were opening paying tin ground. In general, the tin producing part of the mine continued to look favourable, but the copper part was less promising. By May, the accounts were again slightly in the red, with a loss of £74.

The August account proved to be a gloomy affair. The quarter's loss amounted to £382 6s. 5d., bringing the total adverse balance to £2,774 10s. 9d. A call of £2 per 200th share was made. Amounts of tin raised from the different parts of the mine were: Botallack, 61 tons 15 cwt. for £2,425 1s.; Truthwall, 25 tons 1 cwt. for £1,044 8s.; Carnyorth, 22 tons 14 cwt. for £868 2s. In addition, copper had been sold to the value of £123 1s., whilst arsenic on account was valued at £200. About 220 men and boys were employed at Botallack, and there were 71 adventurers, 30 of whom held single shares.

The Purser stated that during the past year they had raised £20,000 worth of minerals, and in spite of the present quarter's loss had only fallen short of their twelve months' cost by £225. Tin, during that quarter, had sold for only £39 12s. 6d. per ton, compared with £41 8s. during the previous three months. One shareholder paid a handsome compliment to Mr. James for his indefatigable efforts on behalf of the mine, "though heavy clouds at present hung over it". Another was equally complimentary towards the agents: "There could not be better nor more energetic men than . . . Capts. Frank Bennetts, Rowe and Hocking, or a better tin-dresser (as was his father before him) than Capt. James Thomas." The Purser: "They are all graduates of Ding Dong." (Laughter). Capt.

15. Wooden Headgear at Wheal Cock Shaft after re-collaring. Bridle with pump in shaft & pump motor can be seen on far side of the shaft. Note the electricity supply to the shaft for pumps. (Early 1908)

*16. Wheal Cock Engine Shaft. Pump motor fixed onto pump within bridle frame.
Cables from Botallack powerhouse can be seen in top foreground. (Early 1908)*

17. Ninevahs Shaft. Preparations were being made to install high-lift pumps in late 1907 or early 1908. Steam hoist with vertical boiler & stack in centre of picture. Note, electricity cables on poles by shaft. (1907/8)

18. *Water tanks for dressing ore centre right. On left in middle distance is the piston for a winder. Winder-compressor house being erected in front of Allens Shaft, with a small sinking headframe. Stamps frames being erected in left background with old chimney stack behind. (Oct-Dec 1907)*

Bennetts, after complaining bitterly of the low price of tin, thought it not at all unlikely that between the 150 and 180 in Carnyorth they might find a splendid piece of tin ground 30 fathoms high and of great length; but it was hard work to do anything with tin at £40 a ton, unless every part of the mine was as easily worked as Wheal Loor, where they had broken ground at 20s. a fathom, which would turn out a ton of tin to the fathom.[4]

A slightly lower loss (£245 2s.) was sustained in November, this being attributed in part to the dry weather and lower price of coal, which had lessened their cost for this article. The 180 E. on Wheal Loor lode had been driving, and the men were now rising to communicate with a winze sinking under the 150 E., which was down about 13 fathoms in paying tin ground. A rise over the 110 cross-cut N., on what was believed to be Wheal Chase lode was producing rich stones of tin. At the Bussa, the 100 driving E. on a side lode and rise over this level were in paying tin ground. The 10 N. on Corpus Christi at the Bussa had been communicated to Botallack adit; this would relieve the pumping engine of a large body of water. At Wheal Cock, the 100 S. on Corpus Christi and a rise over it were producing rich stones of copper. The 100 W . in Carnyorth on New Lode was driving in good tin ground. Capt. Bennetts summarised the quarter's working by saying that "they had obtained less money for more tin."

A call of £2 10s. was made per share in February 1878, to offset the quarter's loss of £467. 110 tons of tin were sold 7 cwt. more than the previous quarter, but it realised £150 less, the average price received now being only £37 15s. per ton. Speaking after the dinner, Mr. James remarked that if the price of tin had warranted it, they could have sold more, and thus reduced the adverse balance. A discussion followed on the alleged distress among the western miners. During this, the purser announced that they had 125 men and 39 boys on tutwork, and, counting two boys as one man, their average earnings amounted to 57s. 6d. a month per man, clear of doctor and club. They had 58 men and 14 boys on tribute, who averaged 50s. each, also exclusive of doctor and club. Their surface workers were still being paid the same wages as in 1865. Complaints were made of inaccurate and exaggerated official statements regarding the distress among the miners. Mr. Chenhalls remarked that the real pinch in St. Just arose from the fact that, whilst the average wage was a fair one, and almost liberal in view of the price of tin, yet it was lower by £1 a month than it used to be, and miners were called upon to work so much harder to secure their money with less animal food to sustain them. Capt. Bennetts said he did not think that the men were more worn by the labour than formerly, but much money spent on ribbons in the parish might with advantage go in beef—an observation that was greeted with laughter.[5]

The accounts were almost balanced again in May, there being a loss of only £47 17s. The agents reported that in Higher Mine the 180 on Wheal Loor was driving and poor, but promising. The 170 E. and W. were both opening good tin

81

ground. In Wheal Cock, the 100 S. was a promising end, and driving towards Higher Mine, where the lode was very productive. The Purser remarked that their accounts presented a much better state of things than he had anticipated, despite a further drop of £1 15s. in the price of tin. Still, it was very disheartening to have to raise and sell 123 tons of tin at this price, but to do so and then nearly meet costs was a thing he had never anticipated. The price of copper was also down, but he thought the old mine would pull through. Capt. Bennetts stated that the ground opened lately had turned out remarkably well, and unless there was some heavy breakage or unforeseen misfortune, he believed the next three months would be as good as the last. Mr. E. H. Rodd wistfully recalled the days when he had received £720 in dividends in one year from Botallack; which led Mr. James to observe that the mine then divided as profit 13s. 4d. out of every £ the minerals realised. Mr. F. Boase, speaking of the services rendered by the committee, said they had called on the shareholders for £6,000—£30 on each of the 200 shares, spread over many years. For this outlay, they had the ample satisfaction of knowing that they had kept a large number of men in employ.

"As things go" (wrote the *Cornish Telegraph* of August 27th, reporting the next meeting) "the quarterly account of this grand old mine … was of a most satisfactory character, for the esteemed purser was able to show as small a loss as £30 on the three months' working; and the agents were in a position to report an improvement in the mine and everything on it in good working order." A cross-cut at the 150 in Higher Mine driving in the S. wall on a guide had encountered the best tin ground found on Wheal Loor lode. Should the ground continue fair for driving, the agents advised prosecuting the cross-course with all speed, as in 60 fathoms it would cut the Bussa lode 90 fathoms further E. than it had been seen at that level. In Wheal Cock, the 135 and 112 driving N., and a rise over the 112, were opening very promising ground. The lode was taking a different course from others worked in this section, and had not been seen at the shallower levels. Its further development was thought desirable. The winze sinking under the 88 W. at Carnyorth had been in good tin ground. Mr. F. Boase suggested that since the mine was so well managed, the adventurers would not object to a small call for a boring machine, which, if it did not work much cheaper, would get out the stuff four times as fast as hand labour. His idea was not then adopted, however. Capt. Bennetts told the meeting that their tin prospects were as good as he had ever known them, and during the seven years he had been on the mine they had never raised as much tin, and at so small a cost, as in the last six months. The Purser announced that a trial of Sholl's Pneumatic stamps held on the mine had been a great success; and the surface agent, Capt. J. Thomas, described the stamps as "a very pretty machine, with a nice motion". A ton of stuff an hour was passed through, equal to 24 heads of the ordinary stamps, but it did not stamp the stuff fine enough for Botallack tin, "which required to be broken so fine that the grain could not be felt between the fingers". They tried finer grates, but neither would answer. Then "floshes" were suggested, and with the stamp heads making from 140-150 blows a minute, they floshed as well as the old stamps. Of course, with floshes the pneumatic stamps would not do as large a quantity, but they then did equal to 16 heads of ordinary stamps. These improved stamps were adopted by Botallack, giving the mine a technical lead over all others at St. Just in this respect. A committee member asked, if, in view of a recent dispute at Wheal Seton, they let their tin leavings to anyone below them. Capt. James replied that they worked their leavings three times over themselves; two of these did not pay, but they acted as "detectives".

The November meeting saw the accounts almost exactly balanced. The openings were much the same as last reported, but the stopes were not producing as much tin. The average price of tin sold that quarter was the lowest recorded in the present working of the mine, being nearly £2 per ton less than the previous quarter. The question of the boring machine was again raised, but the meeting decided to defer the matter until a new lease of Wheal Cock had been settled. Mr. F. Boase, in reminiscent mood, recalled that at one time Botallack "was regarded as a sort of dockyard affair, where all sorts of extravagances were allowed, but (now) there was really no mine in Cornwall in which economy was more closely allied with efficiency". This, needless to say, was one of the few ben/eficial results of the abysmally low price of tin. Mr. T. W. Field confirmed this view, observing that when tin was £100 a ton, agents had no control over men, and there was great extravagance in working.

In his final report on Botallack, dated December 24, Warrington Smyth stated that the shaft arrangements at Wheal Cock had been much improved. A new lode branching off more Easterly than the others was being followed up from the land workings towards and under the sea in three of the deeper levels; it was here that most of the royalties had been earned for above a year past. The 135 fathom level showed a lode only 6-8 inches wide with very little tin and copper; but the 112, now out 24 fathoms beyond high water mark, was in parts 2 feet wide and yielded a fair amount of those ores. At the moment, the end was small and the rock dark and hard. At the 100, some tin was being raised from above the same place. He continued: "I went through the old workings at the 20, where by climbing up into the 'backs' you reach the place beneath the sea, where above half a century ago two boreholes were put upwards to the sea bottom and were immediately stopped with plugs of wood. The ground has been no further worked since, and the plugs with their fibres saturated with water appear to be secure enough. But as the removal of one of these plugs would drown the whole mine, Mr. James has it in contemplation to shut off this place from access.

A loss of £157 2s. 4d. was announced at the February 1879 account. 120 tons of tin had realised £3,947 11s. arsenic £103 6s. and copper ore for sale £250. In Higher Mine, the cross-cut at the 150 E. driving S. towards the Bussa was now in about 45 fathoms, ground favourable for driving. At Wheal Cock the 112 S. was driving and producing some rich grey copper ore. There was every indication of a bunch about this place. On New Lode at Carnyorth the 100 and 64 were driving W. and producing a little tin. Purser James remarked they had lately had "an immense amount of difficulty to contend with owing to the immense downfall of rain, and to frost and snow". One of the agents, he added, was laid up owing to continually walking through cold water underground.

The quarterly loss in May proved to be somewhat less—£60. Stopes had fallen off in value, and turned the scales on the wrong side. No call was made, though the debit balance had increased to nearly £3,000. The agents reported the 135 and 112 driving N. in Wheal Cock for tin, copper and arsenic. "It is on this N. and S. lode that we propose working a Boring Machine. Ground very hard, lode in new ground is promising." Their report also contained the rather cryptic sentence: "Owing to increase of water in Higher Mine, we have recovered pitwork, this has been expensive." This section, however, remained in active production. In August, the loss was up again to £444. "The mine continues to make good returns of tin, but it is the price that kills." A call of £2 10s. was made, which they hoped would be the last, as the prospects appeared better than for many years. At Higher Mine, the cross-cut driving S. on the 150 E. had now advanced more than 60 fathoms, and was hoped would intersect the Bussa in 10 fathoms further driving. The agents had contracted for driving the 112 N. by boring machine in Wheal Cock. In the 112 S. the E. and W. lode had been intersected, its eastern end opening paying tin ground. Concerning the decision to install the boring machine, the *Cornish Telegraph* congratulated purser, agents, and committee "on having been the first to introduce so far west the more rapid means of development already adopted with such signal success by their neighbours eastward".

In their July-September report (presented at the November account) the agents stated that the cross-cut S. at the 150 in Higher Mine towards the Bussa had cut a lode with spar and a little tin, but they had not seen much of it. In Wheal Cock the 112 N. had been driven by boring machine for a distance of 22 fathoms, but had produced nothing to value. At Carnyorth, they propose to resume sinking Nineveh Shaft, suspended some years before. This was considered promising, as the bottom level here (Western Carnyorth) was driven through 100 fathoms of tin ground which had paid to stope. The financial details for this quarter have not been traced; but in February 1880, the figures were: expenditure, £4,800; credits, £6,096, including £1,340 on sale of stocked tin; actual profit, £827; balance against the mine, £1,727. It was resolved to sub divide the shares from 200 to 800. The agents' report was a very favourable one. At the 170 E. in Higher Mine there was a fair lode in the bottom of the end. The Bussa had now definitely been intersected at the 150 cross-cut S., lode poor. Engine Shaft was cleared to the 205, and they intended sinking as soon as possible—a notable sign, this, of increased confidence. At Wheal Cock they were preparing to sink Skip Shaft under the 150, on the North lode. At the 112, 50 fathoms had been driven by rock boring machine, the winze under this level producing tin and arsenic, whilst the rise over was giving some rich grey copper ore. At Carnyorth, Nineveh Shaft had been sunk to the 64.

Some interesting reports were published in May regarding the use of rock drills machinery in the St. Just mines. It had at first been thought that the lodes there were too small to justify their use, but two drills were now at work—one at Botallack, and the other at Wheal Owles. The first was worked by steam, and the latter by water "where, unfortunately, such power cannot with certainty be depended on throughout the summer months, but we understand that both machines at present are working to the satisfaction of the agents".[6] It appears that the machine used at Botallack was the "Eclipse", and that the contract with Capt. Henderson for working it was terminated that month. Levant joined the march of progress at this time, by contracting with the patentees of the "Beaumont" drill

In their report covering January-March the agents expressed doubts whether the lode found in the 150 cross-cut S. at Higher Mine was, in fact, the Bussa. In Wheal Cock, Skip Shaft had been sunk for a plot 4 fathoms under the 150. They proposed driving N. and S. at this level with rock borer as soon as the tram road had been completed. The end driven by rock borer at the 112 N., poor, had been suspended. At Carnyorth Nineveh Shaft was sinking under the 64. A breakage at the steam stamps had delayed tin returns and entailed great expense. Some further difficulties, but of a different character, occurred in June, when a good deal of tutwork was suspended; several of the men were offered tribute instead, but refused to take it in the captain's price. The August meeting showed a profit of £543, reducing the debit balance to £1,373. Over 100 tons of tin had been raised, selling at an average price of about £52 a ton. At Higher Mine, the end driving S. in the 150 had opened paying tin ground in a lode which the agents did not think had been seen before. The cross-cut S. towards the S. was still driving. At Wheal Cock, the 150 had been opened, and a tram road laid to within 15 fathoms of the end. They hoped soon to have a rock borer working there.

In February 1881, the Purser issued a circular stating that in consequence of the heavy fall of snow and severe frost, all dressing operations at surface and drawing of stuff from underground, had been suspended for a fortnight, so that no returns were made. Under these circumstances, the committee thought it better to postpone the quarterly meeting, fixed for February, to May 18th. The latter was therefore a six-months' account, the figures being: labour, £5,652; materials, £1,098; coal, £884; carriage, £437; total costs, £8,303. 141 tons of tin, £7,194; copper, £758; arsenic, £143; sundries, £77. Loss on six months, £131. At Higher Mine, the lode under the 150 fathom level was reported very rich. A cross-cut was being driven at the 150 N. in Wheal Cock by a rock-borer to intersect a winze sinking under the 135 N. on another lode, and which was in paying ground for tin and arsenic. They hoped soon to cut the E. and W. lode seen in the 112, and which had disorganised the lode at that level. The 30 N. had been suspended; they had driven through a rich lode of copper at this level for about ten fathoms, but the ore only held for a few feet above and below the level. In Carnyorth, men were cutting down and fixing skip road to Nineveh Shaft. Capt. Bennetts said that although the mine was not looking so well, he still believed they had good chances before them. Botallack was not like many mines where the making of tin depended on the congenial strata of the ground, for if their lodes were poor the ground was of the same character as where they were rich. Tin had fallen in price since nine months before. Mr. James said it was not pleasant to see the mine going to leeward and he was sorry to say her prospects were poor. Nevertheless, he still hoped for some good discoveries.[7]

The loss on the November quarter was £569 14s. In Higher Mine, the 180 E. was driving, lode small and poor. The 150 E. had been suspended, as the end was hard, and the lode small and without tin. In the 150 cross-cut S. the men had been opening westward on the lode cut some time since, but as it had proved valueless they had resumed driving the cross-cut. Engine Shaft was now sunk about 6 fathoms below the 205, lode of good quality tinstuff and ground favourable for sinking. At Wheal Cock, the 150 N. had been driven by rock-borer 20 fathoms since last meeting; the greater part had opened good tin ground, the end worth £15 per fathom. The 150 being the bottom level, they had thought it advisable to sink the Skip Shaft. The ground in Nineveh Shaft at Carnyorth had proved much harder than anticipated, and little progress had been made. The agents regretted the poor returns of tin, but pointed out that the ends looked most promising … Mr. James confirmed the latter point, adding that it had been reported to him that morning that the lode going S. from the 150 cross-cut in Wheal Cock was of a very good condition. He thought the mine was looking considerably better than for some time. But for the boring machine they would never have found the lode in Wheal Cock. The machine was doing good duty, and if they wished to extend its operations to Higher Botallack, this could be done with very little outlay; all that would be wanted was a few pipes and a compressor.

The February, 1882, account, revealed a further loss, of £448 5s. and a call of £1 was made. Only 53 tons of tin had been sold, for £3,443 13s. 4d.—a sad decline on earlier years. Engine Shaft at Higher Mine was 10 fathoms under the 205, producing tin, but barely sufficient to pay. One of two winzes sunk 8 fathoms below the 205, however, was in payable tin ground; it lay within 20 fathoms of the shaft. Both had been stopped on account of the water. At Wheal Loor (now, apparently, considered to be a separate section) the end driving W. on Parknoweth at the 130 was producing good stones of tin, but the ground was too hard to be profitable. Skip Shaft at Wheal Cock was 12 fathoms below the 150, producing good stones of copper. The 150 N. driving by rock borer was opening good paying tin ground. A winze sinking under the 155 had been communicated to this end, opening up good stoping ground. At Carnyorth, Minerva Shaft[8] was sinking under the 100, lode large and going through ground that would pay to work. It was intended to clear Engine Shaft to the bottom to resume driving the bottom levels. Ground opened in three months was 105 fathoms. 60 men and 17 boys were opening; and 80 men and 13 boys stoping ground on tut and tribute. The Purser paid tribute to a "valuable servant" who had died since their last meeting—Capt. Frank Bennetts. Capt. James Roach, late of Wheal Owles, who had been appointed to succeed him, told the adventurers that in his view Botallack, with other mines, had suffered from mistaken measures of false economy, and in Higher Mine very little exploratory work had been carried out for some time. The pumping engine had been working to its full extent, but they proposed to double its efficiency by disconnecting some of the upper lifts, so making available sufficient power to go from 50 to 80 fathoms deeper. At Carnyorth, the deepest level drained was the 100, and a great part of the workable ground had been taken away. It had been decided to clear the mine to bottom, and drive the deeper levels W. under Nineveh Shaft where valuable tin ground was believed to exist. Wheal Cock was a hard ground mine, where rock borers could be used to advantage. Capt. Roach was pleased at a decision taken that day to purchase another one. The lode in Wheal Cock was "bunchy", but he thought she would do the adventurers some good eventually. They were preparing to clear the water out of its northern part, and the additional cost of working this would only be for labour, as they had pumping and hauling power at command. Capt. Rowe defended the memory of the late Capt. Bennetts, who, by implication, had been criticised by Capt. Roach's strictures on the lack of recent exploratory work. "During the time that Capt. Bennetts was managing the mine it was very hard uphill work. The price of tin was down, and everything seemed to be quite against the mine. They were, therefore, compelled to confine their operations to those points ... best calculated to help them meet the pressing emergency." These points were in Wheal Loor, where a great deal had been done at a profit, but the ends were poor now. In the 180 at Carnyorth they had driven 100 fathoms without finding sufficient mineral to pay for the candles burnt there. Such a case was hardly to be paralleled in the county. The bottom of the mine seemed to offer the best chance of success. With tin at £70, he thought if the adventurers had a little more patience, the mine would be set on a satisfactory basis.

On April 20th it was reported that a good lode of copper had been cut in Wheal Cock Skip Shaft, valued at £70-80 per fathom for the width of the shaft. It would, however, be some weeks before sinking could be recommenced. The shaft lay 20 fathoms E. of Engine Shaft, which was sunk to the 150. Skip Shaft was 15 fathoms deeper, with a considerable quantity of water in it, and rods and pumps would have to be fixed to draw it out. In their March report the agents stated that Engine Shaft at Higher Mine had been sunk 16 fathoms under the 205, lode without tin. The 130 and 140 E. on Wheal Loor were poor, and the 180 E. also unremunerative. In view of these facts, they felt uncertain whether to recommend sinking Engine Shaft further. The engine was not of sufficient power to go deeper, and continuing would necessitate a new and larger engine and pitwork, as well as a man-engine, on account of the depth. These observations, it may be noted, strangely contradict Capt. Roach's optimistic remarks on the engine at the February meeting. At Wheal Cock, Skip Shaft was sunk 15 fathoms under the 150. Tolven Shaft was in fork and cleared 35 fathoms below adit. When the water was down 70 fathoms they would continue the 70 cross cut in Wheal Cock to intersect the North lode, and by communicating also with Tolven Mine, ventilate this part of Wheal Cock. At Carnyorth, Nineveh Shaft was down 9 fathoms below the 100. There were 73 men and 16 boys opening, and 98 men and 9 boys stoping on tut and tribute.

Presumably, as a consequence of the agents' doubts regarding Higher Mine, Lord Falmouth consented during the latter part of May to allow the shareholders to abandon the deeper levels, so as to more vigorously prosecute the shallow ones there, and Wheal Cock and Carnyorth. It would have been impossible to go deeper without an expenditure of at least £10,000. At a four-monthly account held on August 16th a loss of £1,887 7s. was announced, increasing the adverse balance to £5,511 2s. A call of £2 10s. per share was made. The interest of Messrs. Davy in the mine had been acquired by Messrs. Bolitho, this event necessitating the appointment of a new committee consisting of F. Boase, H. Thomas, W. Holman, and J. B. Coulson. At Wheal Cock the 150 W. had been driving by rock borer; it had gone through about 15 fathoms of good paying tin ground, but the last ten fathoms had been poor. At Carnyorth, the lode in the 112 driving E. and W. was of a most kindly appearance. During the quarter an engine house had been erected and engine fixed to draw from Nineveh Shaft. They hoped to have everything completed in another fortnight. In Higher Botallack, the men were clearing the adit and 60 fathom level.[9]

At the February account for 1883, the quarter's loss amounted to £1,740 19s. 7d. Tin realised £2,546, arsenic and sundries £117, and a call of £2 was made. Mr. S. H. James said he had seen Botallack look as poor as it did now more than once in times past, but, "as they weathered the storm, it came good again", and they must hope it would be so in the future. Despite his optimism, affairs looked even grimmer at the May meeting. The loss then amounted to £1,970, whilst during the quarter only 36 tons 5 cwt. of tin had been sold, worth £1,917. A further call of £2 was made. All relinquished or forfeited shares were to be placed to an account, and disposed of as the committee might determine. Twelve shares belonging to three adventurers were declared forfeit. The agents, however, were able to offer some encouragement. Wheal Cock Skip Shaft sinking under the 160 had been in good tin ground, and, though not so rich as it had been, was worth £25 per fathom for the length of the shaft. The 160 N. was driving towards Engine Shaft, which was sinking under the 150, both openings unproductive. In Carnyorth, a winze sinking under the 42 W . on New Lode to communicate to a rise over the 64 was opening paying ground. The 60 E. on Wheal Loor in Higher Mine was producing tin.

On June 28th, it was stated that Botallack shares had advanced, being quoted at £5-7, the prospects having improved, but at the August account it really seemed as if the mine had reached the end of the road. The cost book showed: expenses, £4,100; receipts, £2,504; loss on three months, £1,596. £1,480 had been received from calls and relinquished shares, and the balance against the mine stood at £5,984. A call of £4 per share (£3,200) was made; and it was resolved to offer Botallack as a going concern. A special meeting was convened for the 30th August to consider this resolution. Mr. James, however, declared that under any circumstances he would continue his interest in the mine, for he believed that just as Dolcoath had produced first tin, and then copper, then tin again, so, if they sunk Wheal Cock, which had produced such rich bunches of copper, they would eventually have a good tin mine. But such courage and optimism were clearly at a premium in that account house on such a black and sorrowful day.

1 *Cornish Telegraph*, August 26th and September 9th 1874.
2 *Cornish Telegraph,* January 20th 1875.
3 See D. B. Barton's *Essays in Cornish Mining History* (Volume 2) 1970.
4 *Cornish Telegraph,* August 21st 1877.
5 *Cornish Telegraph,* February 26th 1878.
6 *Cornish Telegraph,* May 19th 1880.
7 *Cornish Telegraph*, May 26th 1881.
8 This name is not otherwise recorded; it appears to be an erroneous rendering of *Nineveh* Shaft.
9 *Cornish Telegraph*, August 24th 1882.

BOTALLACK MINE COST FOR JULY AND AUGUST 1855.

ACCOUNT HELD ON THE MINE 16TH OCTOBER, 1855.

Dr.	£	s.	d.	Cr.		£	s.	d.
To Labour Cost	1651	17	3	By Copper Ore Sold July and August,				
To Carriage	194	12	10	157T. 1c. 2QRS..........£ 2494 18 8				
To Coals ex Ships	199	7	10	Less Dues 1—18th.... 138 12 1				
To Merchants' Bills, &c	787	17	2			2356	6	7
To Shipping Ores	5	3	4	By Tin Sold 24T.15c.1Q.23L.£ 1805 5 10				
				Less Dues 1—24th..... 75 4 4				
	£2838	18	5			1730	1	6
To Profit	1393	2	1	By Sundry Credits		145	12	5
	£4232	0	6			£4232	0	6
October 16th.,								
To Dividend this day of £7 per each ..)	1400	0	0	By Profit		1393	2	1
1—200th Share)								
To Balance to next Account	2017	10	8	By Balance from last Account		2024	8	7
	£3417	10	8			£3417	10	8
				By Balance to credit of Adventurers......£2017	10	8		

The next Account will be held on the Mine on Tuesday 18th day of December at Noon.

A copy of the cost sheet for two months in 1855, signed by S. H. James, the purser.

Chapter Six:
The Road to Ruin

The meeting on August 30th, held at the Union Hotel in Penzance, again resolved to try and sell the mine. But it was also decided to convene another special meeting for September 14th to confirm or change this resolution. It was, in the event, confirmed, the date of sale being fixed for October 2nd. The adventurers were, however, informed that the Carnyorth section was looking better, whilst in Wheal Cock Engine Shaft the tin lode had much improved, tributers there at 5s. 6d. in the £ having had a good "sturt," breaking nearly two tons in a week. At the sale, also held at the Union Hotel, no bid was made for the mine. Capt. Roach told those who attended that there was a good, strong, well-defined lode in the bottom of Wheal Cock. Mr. Boase expressed the belief that if £25,000 were spent to put Botallack in good order she would again prove rich. The lord, he added, might have been more liberal in the matter of dues, the present shareholders had gone on for eleven years without dividends and making calls, and as a great many shares had passed to the hands of trustees there was difficulty in getting the calls paid.

A further meeting was decided on to consider whether the enterprise should be continued or not now that no buyer could be found. No report of this has been found; but it is clear from subsequent notices that the adventurers resolved to soldier on. It was a decision they must all have subsequently regretted; for this final phase of cost-book working was to prove an unmitigated misfortune to all connected with it. In their September report (for November) the agents stated they considered the bottom of Wheal Cock worth developing. The lodes formerly worked on were in the eastern wall of Skip Shaft; it would take three months to cross-cut to these with a rock-borer. They also recommended driving the 124 W. at Carnyorth as there had been a good run of tin ground at the 112.

A report dated January 31st 1884, spoke of a lode recently cut in the mine, worth £70 per fathom. This was cheering news; but the shareholders had to face less palatable facts at the February account. The loss on three months amounted to £225, increasing the total adverse balance to £4,167. No call was made, and it was agreed to apply to the lord for a remission of dues in consequence of the large outlay made during 1883. At Wheal Cock, Skip Shaft had been sunk six fathoms under the 170, lode large, and worth about £10 per fathom. At Wheal Cock the 112 W. was driving by rock borer, lode averaging £10 per fathom; this level had been driven through ground of the same value for the last 30 fathoms. The mine's prospects, it was thought, were improving. There were 41 men and 3 boys opening, and 84 men and 8 boys stoping ground on tribute. In his speech, the Purser remarked on the good work done by their boring machine; it had opened out much good ground during the month. Speaking of his own personal position, he remarked that the office he held had not been an enviable one for many years, for he had been continually dunning people to pay their calls, some being personal friends; but in only one instance had he received an unkind word. In few mines had calls been better paid than Botallack, and he hoped by next account there would not be a single defaulter. Capt. Roach spoke very hopefully of the future; the mine was looking better than he had ever seen it before. In the lower part of Carnyorth they had sunk 24 fathoms below the former workings, and had opened up a payable lode. They were working the boring machine there, but did not get more than a man's labour for every horse-power employed, and as one horse could do the work of seven men, there appeared to be very great waste. Nevertheless, the machine had been of great advantage in opening up that piece of ground.[1]

In their March report, however, the agents regretted there had been no improvement in the mine. They had 44 men and 7 boys opening and 78 men and 7 boys stoping ground on tut and tribute. The August account made bleak reading. There had been a loss of £948, though £350 worth of tin remained unstamped owing to the drought. Tin sold amounted to 59 tons, which realised from £45-48 a ton. A call of £1 was made. At Wheal Cock, Skip Shaft was 12 fathoms under the 170, and sinking for a fork. The lode was large, and contained tin, but did not pay to work. In Carnyorth, Nineveh Shaft was 5 fathoms under the 124, lode 2 feet wide, and worth £9 per fathom. It was maintained that the loss that quarter had been sustained by sinking these shafts and operating the rock borer. In November another call of £1 was asked for to meet a further loss of £545. Of the tin sales, 27 tons 15 cwt. came from Botallack (i.e., Wheal Cock) and 24 tons 5 cwt. from Carnyorth. The price received for it was £3 7s. 6d. per ton less than last quarter, and £10 less than in the corresponding period for 1883. Wheal Cock Skip Shaft was now sunk to the 180; they were driving N. and S. in that level, lode in each 3 feet wide, worth £5 for tin. Nineveh Shaft was 10 fathoms under the 124 in Carnyorth, lode much improved, and worth £14 for length of shaft (11 feet). The 112 E. driving by rock borer was poor. Higher Botallack made a reappearance in this report; some tributers were at work there driving an end S. at the adit.

Only the agents' reports are available for the next three quarters. In December, they announced Nineveh Shaft sinking under the 136, lode worth £13 for length of shaft. The 136 level was driving W. by rock borer, worth £6, whilst the 136 E. had opened tribute ground, but the lode was disordered. In Higher Botallack, the adit end driving S. was worth £5 in easy ground, and would work at half-tribute. In March 1885, they reported the 170 S. Wheal Cock in granite, lode worth £4. At Carnyorth, Nineveh Shaft was sinking under the 136, lode 2 feet wide and worth £12 for length of shaft; this would pay for sinking. The 136 E. was unproductive. The 136 W., driving by rock borer, was also barren. A lode here—believed to be the Nogger—had split off from it, but they hoped to recover the run of tin as soon as a winze sinking under the 124 had been communicated. Activity at Higher Botallack was increasing; the 60 driving S. on Scorran was worth £4. The adit S. on this lode was unproductive, but they looked for an early improvement here. An end driving W. of Engine Shaft at the adit was valued at £5. The men had been clearing adits and shallow levels in this section, and laying open tribute ground. June saw Nineveh Shaft 11 fathoms under the 136. They would soon commence driving ends and prepare to sink another lift. A winze under the 136 W. was in good tin ground, worth £20. At Higher Mine the 60 S. on Scorran had opened tribute ground. Their labour force was now increasing again, 50 men and one boy opening, and 89 men and 13 boys stoping on tut and tribute. The November account read: Labour, £2,337 8s. 6d.; cost and carriage of coal, £449 15s 10d.; merchants' bills, £431 3s. 2d.; bank charges, £50; stamps' rents, £33 8s. 7d.; sundries, £11 19s. 8d.; tin sold, 59 tons, £3,051 3s.8d.; copper, £71 13s. 11d.; arsenic, £46 13s. 4d.; sundry credits, £15 0s. 1d.; loss on 13 weeks, £129 4s. 9d.; total adverse balance, £3,771 11s. 6d. Mr. James said they might have shown a clear sheet that day but for a breakage of the stamps' axle, which threw them back a little in returns. At Wheal Cock the 135 S. was driving in easy ground to get under a course of ground gone down under the 125 about 18 fathoms in advance of the end. Nineveh Shaft at Carnyorth had been completed to the 140, and the ends at this level driven about 15 fathoms E. and W. The rock borer was advancing the latter end, and in about a month they hoped to reach the tin ground gone down under the 136. The shaft men were preparing to sink under the 148.

The meeting held on February 18th 1886, showed a small profit, of £22 8s. Capts. J. Roach and M. Thomas reported that the 160 and 170 N. at Wheal Cock were worth £4 per fathom, ends very promising. At Carnyorth, Nineveh Shaft had been sunk by rock borer under the 148; it was already down 7 fathoms, shaft improving, and producing a little tin. The 148 W. had been driven W. 40 fathoms, almost entirely through good tin ground, though the end was now poor. A winze sinking under this level was valued at £15 per fathom. They had increased their returns of tin, the additional metal coming from Carnyorth; but the manager could hold out only faint hopes about Wheal Cock. Another small profit (£51 8s.) was announced in May. The tin sold amounted to 74 tons 15 cwt., realising £4,016 6s. At Wheal Cock the 135 S. had been driven through some good tin and copper ground, one pitch there being worth £16 per fathom. A winze sinking under the 125 in advance of this end, worth £25 per fathom, had been suspended on account of water. They hoped to get under this by the rock borer in 3-4 months. The agents also advised driving the 160 S. by rock borer to this place, and ultimately to continue this level to Carnyorth, so proving a large piece of unexplored ground, and unwatering the workings around Nineveh Shaft. In

Carnyorth, Nineveh Shaft had been sunk and completed to the 160, the bottom being in paying ground. In his after dinner speech, Mr. James said they had "turned the corner", adding that they had been treated with a good deal of consideration by Lord Falmouth and the other mineral owners. He thought if the lords had not done so they would not have met around that table that day. Lord Falmouth and others had not only given up dues, but had allowed dues to accumulate from previous accounts. Capt. Roach stated they were about to explore a piece of virgin ground in Wheal Cock, of which good things had been predicted. He mentioned that during the quarter they had spent £1,200 in working their boring machinery—proving that they worked in a very proper manner.[2]

September saw the mine's affairs looking better than for some time past. 91 tons 15 cwt. of tin had realised £5,199; copper ore, £76; and arsenic £86; the profit on 16 weeks being £240, reducing the balance against the adventurers to £3,427 11s. At Wheal Cock, a trial winze sinking under the 150 N. 80 fathoms further N. than any of the deeper levels was worth £10 per fathom. At Carnyorth, Nineveh Shaft was sinking by rock borer under the 160, down 11 fathoms, 9 of these through good tin ground. There had been a split in the lode, however, and the end was now poor. The adit driving in the Scorran S. of Parknoweth lode in Higher mine was expected soon to intersect the Bussa.

The account held in August was of a very encouraging nature. The cost book showed a profit of £1,012, reducing the adverse balance to £526. 112 tons 12 cwt. of tin had been raised, worth £6,748, less dues. Capt. Roach said they would have made an even greater profit but for the large sum spent on machinery, and in increasing the reserves—i.e., by development work—to improve the condition of the mine. There were two boring machines at work, and they hoped soon to have a third. His comments on the mine's prospects were, however, not too optimistic. The bottom of Nineveh was not looking so well. In the N. part of Wheal Cock they had been sinking and driving, but had to go a long way from the shaft and sink a trial winze at the bottom; they had sunk this, and driven, and found some mineral ground. Now things did not look so bright, as this could not be opened quickly enough, and a boring machine would probably have to be used there. The Purser stated that at Wheal Cock, tin ground had been opened up which they had no reason to expect. The point at which it was hoped to find the mineral had not yet been reached. An enormous sum of money had been laid out in reconstructing their machinery. The agents reported the 170 N. at Wheal Cock holed to Engine Shaft. At Carnyorth, Nineveh Shaft, completed to the 180, was beginning to sink another lift. The 180 had been driven 4 fathoms E. in good tin ground, the western end also in good tin ground, but the lode at present disordered.

In November, it was reported they had 68 men and 11 boys opening and 101 men and 8 boys stoping ground on tribute. During that month there occurred a melancholy event, which cast a gloom over the mine's affairs. This was the death (at Penzance) of Stephen Harvey James, who had faithfully served Botallack as Purser since the death of his father in 1870. He had seen the mine undergo many vicissitudes, alternating between dividends and calls, but he never lost faith in it. His death occurred at a particularly unfortunate moment, for there seemed every prospect that his patience and energy were about to be rewarded. At the next account the last remnant of the adverse balance which had so long confronted the adventurers would be swept away, justifying his confidence in the resources of Botallack.[3]

Mr. James was succeeded as Purser and Manager by his son, Arthur Harvey James. Thus, four generations of this family—commencing with old Jaketh James—played a leading role at Botallack, the last three being in effectual command of the mine. This is an interesting dynastic mining association which it would be hard to parallel in Cornwall. A. H. James was to show himself a worthy successor to his distinguished forebears. He prosecuted the mine with the utmost vigour and determination, almost succeeding in restoring Botallack to the dividend list. But a combination of adverse circumstances, including a serious accident, and a disastrous fall in the price of tin, eventually undermined his efforts and brought the mine to ruin. Nothing but a large transfusion of new capital could have averted this catastrophe, and that was not forthcoming.

At the December meeting a determined attempt was made by one shareholder to get the existing method of selling tin direct to smelters (Bolitho and Field) who were large shareholders in the mine replaced by the more conventional ticketing system. The Chairman, however, would promise no more than that the committee would "consider" the matter. "Of course they will do this" (commented the *Cornish Telegraph*) "but the tone adopted ... by both Mr. Bolitho, M.P., and Mr. Field (doubtless in a conviction that they were acting in the interests of the shareholders) does not augur well for any favourable result ..." The "exclusive" system of selling tin was virtually confined to the St. Just mines, in which the smelters had a strong interest. By abolishing competition, it gave rise to a strong suspicion in the minds of many shareholders that they were getting less than a fair market price for their tin.

The March account for 1888, thanks to the higher price of tin, proved one of the best for some time. The profit amounted to £1,082, and there was a total credit balance of £1,120. Tinsales were 93¼ tons, realising £7,851. The agents reported the 170 W. in Wheal Cock driven 25 fathoms, the 160 N. 16 fathoms, and a rise over the 170, 11 fathoms, by rock drill. This had opened up a piece of ground now working at one-half tribute. The ends N. and S. under the 150 N. towards which the 170 was driving continued to open profitable tin ground. Preparations were being made to drive the 180 under this ground. At Carnyorth, Nineveh Shaft had been sunk to the 190, and the men were driving E. and W., the lode contained tin, but would not pay to work. The 180 E. had been driven 30 fathoms by rock drill, and a rise over it 12 fathoms. This had opened ground working at half tribute. The 170 was being driven by rock drill to communicate with the rise over the 180. At Higher Botallack, the ends E. and W. on the Bussa at the adit had been driving and opening ground worth £6 per fathom.

July saw Carnyorth Engine Shaft forked to the bottom, and the shaft repaired. The mine at this period began to lapse into financial difficulties again, and in October the adventurers applied to the lords for a remission of dues whilst they were paying calls. This was granted, on condition that Nineveh and Wheal Cock Shafts were sunk. In eight fathoms of sinking under the 190, Nineveh Shaft produced tin, but not to pay. Wheal Cock Engine Shaft was sinking under the 170, and an end being driven by rock drill from the bottom of Skip Shaft to communicate. The amount of tinstuff raised in 16 weeks was 4,688 tons, which yielded 36½ lbs. of tin per ton. About 250 fathoms of tram road had been laid. A stone breaker and engine to work it had been purchased, and were at work. A weighbridge was purchased and fixed whilst the calciner had also been renewed. "The low quality of tinstuff in the bottom of Wheal Cock necessitates that it be treated in a wholesale manner and as cheaply as possible. Laying of Tram Road and purchase of Stone Breaker are first steps in this direction. Propose to renew second skip road in Wheal Cock Skip Shaft, which has been idle some years, and have waggons made to remove tinstuff from Shaft to Stamps using horses instead of manual labor. Carrying out of this will prevent reduction in expenses but we hope same quantity of tin will be raised."

The figures of the account presented in February 1889, were: labour, £3,659; coal, £417 10s. carriage, £208 17s.; stamps' rent, £40; bank charges, £30; Stannary assessment, £3 15s.; merchants, £1,060 14s. Cr. arsenic sold, £127; tin sales (86 tons 15 cwt.) £4,803; loss on 16 weeks, £466 11s. They had some unsold copper, which would reduce the loss to £300. During the quarter a second skip road had been fixed at Wheal Cock, and would be completed in about six weeks. The tin dressing floors at the water stamps had been enlarged, so, despite the falling off of tin from Nineveh, the returns had been more than kept up. During the next sixteen weeks a calciner with arsenic chamber, flue and stack would be erected at the steam stamps. A new 16 heads stamps had been fixed there also, and the tin floors enlarged. Until this was done, the returns of tin could not be increased. Answering questions, the Purser gave the cost of a new calciner as £110. Capt. Thomas explained that it would be able to take an extra amount of stuff from Wheal Cock. Another agent (Capt. Rowe) spoke gloomily of Nineveh. The lode there averaged 2½ feet wide, and in some places was as big as 3 feet; at present, however, it was poor, and the prospects were no better than when he first came to the mine.

By June, ends at the bottom of Nineveh Shaft, 204 E. and W., had been driven 14 fathoms, the whole worth £6. A winze 12 fathoms before the eastern end

19. Allens Shaft. Kibble being tipped into a wagon at collar of the shaft. Note wooden headgear with wire stays for added support. Old chimney stack being repaired in background. (Early 1908)

20. *Part of 150 H.P. gas engine being taken into power house. The gas engines were used to generate electricity. The Californian Stamps being erected inside their frames are in the background. (Autumn 1907)*

21. Three gas engines in Botallack power house. Two of the engines were 150 H.P. and the third was 350 H.P. These generated electricity for most of the mine, including pumps, stamps, dressing & calcining. (1908)

22. *Californian Stamps frames for 20 heads. Note shuttering for a further 20 stamps to be added later. These extra 20 heads were never erected. The power house, nearing completion, is in the background. (Sept 1907)*

under the 190, sunk 13 fathoms, was worth £7. When the winze between the 190 and 204 E. was communicated, sinking of the shaft would be recommenced. This communication was necessary for ventilation. This section was looking better than for some time past. At Wheal Cock, both Skip and Engine Shafts were at the 180, the bottom and the level had been driven N. 17 fathoms beyond Engine Shaft in ground worth £6. They had raised 5,480 tons of tinstuff producing 40½ lbs. of tin per ton. The second Wheal Cock skip road had been completed and was working satisfactorily, whilst the calciner was erected and would soon be operating. The new 16 heads stamps were working, and they were now fixing buddles in the tin floors. Eight tons of tin on the floors partially dressed could not be marketed until the calciner and floors had been completed. The lower price of tin that quarter meant a reduction of £300 on tin sold. The mine actually sustained a loss of over £1,000, due entirely to outlay on the extensive new surface works. The principal item of expenditure was for the construction of new arsenic chambers.

At the account held on October 9th, the manager reported a loss of £569 18s. 104 tons 10 cwt. of tin had been sold for £5,452 15s., whilst arsenic realised £91 7s. The shaftsmen at Carnyorth were cutting fork preparatory to sinking under the 204. The 204 E. was driving and opening ground worth £6. The 190 W. had intersected the Guide (cross-course) which had disorganised the lode. At Wheal Cock, they were cutting down Engine Shaft and putting in pitwork before sinking under the 180. The ground at this bottom level was opening very satisfactorily, and so far they had not reached its limits in the sides. Considerable activity was going on in other parts of this section. 6,212 tons of stuff had produced 41½ lbs. of tin to the ton, or say 115 tons. The water stamps being nearly idle through want of water, there was a considerable quantity of stuff there, and also a large accumulation of roughs, estimated to contain altogether about 20 tons of tin. A stamps was erecting to stamp the roughs which it was hoped would be working that month. Both the new calciner and tin floors were working satisfactorily.[4]

Speaking to shareholders at this meeting, Mr. James said their reserves were better than at last account. "We might be driving ends now, but it is not worth while to be driving speculative ends when we have so much ground open. We have very good facilities for taking the stuff away. We could not improve them unless we sunk a new shaft, and it is not worth while to do that yet. I do not remember the mine looking so well all through for years. The bottom of Wheal Cock is the great place. We cannot tell what we have got there until we develop it."

In line with these views, the opening up of the mine was now vigorously prosecuted, the effects of this policy being strikingly reflected in figures presented at the January account, for 1890. Labour costs then amounted to £4,881 13s., about £1,100 more than during the previous quarter. 127 tons 1 cwt. of tin had sold for £6,981 15s., at an average price of £54 18s.—£2 15s. more than last time. Copper sales (39 tons) realised £279 18s. and arsenic (50 tons) £228 18s. A paper profit of £299 3s. was shown on the cost book, but in fact there was not a profit on the working, as tin from stock had been sold. At Carnyorth, Nineveh Shaft was 9 fathoms under the 204, lode large and producing tin, but not in paying quantities. Ends E. and W. of the 204 were driving in paying tin ground. This level had now been driven on for 50 fathoms, all in profitable ground. It was proposed to drive the 170 W. through to Wheal Cock; this would improve ventilation at both mines and take all the water under the 100 to Wheal Cock engine, thus avoiding the necessity of erecting a pumping engine at Nineveh. The 170 end would communicate at Wheal Cock with the 112 fathom level. The depth at Nineveh was reckoned from surface, but that of Wheal Cock from the level of the sea. Wheal Cock Engine Shaft, sinking 5 fathoms under the 180, was not in the same nature ground as the previous lift. The lode was believed to be in the E. wall; this would be ascertained in the next four months. A cross-cut was being driven across the lode between the 170 and 180, and so far it appeared similar to the ground above. The 112 E.—the end that the 170 from Nineveh would communicate—was temporarily suspended, ventilation imperfect. Its end, after being driven through 50 fathoms of poor ground, had been worth £6 per fathom for the last 2 fathoms. There were 75 men and boys opening, and 145 stoping ground. The ground opened in 16 weeks in shafts, levels and winzes was 96 fathoms, and the tinstuff raised and sampled 7,550 tons, producing 121 tons of tin, or about 36 lbs. to the ton. The Purser said it would take about 12 months to communicate Nineveh and Wheal Cock, at a cost of £1,300-1,400. The adventurers agreed to a call of 2s.—"to show the lord"—who had remitted dues—"that they were not getting anything out of it!". They also agreed that Mr. James, who had received no increase in salary at the time he became Purser and Manager, should have his remuneration increased from eight guineas per month to fifteen, in recognition of his services. When he took over two years ago they were losing about £1,500 per quarter, and things seemed to be going from bad to worse, but he "had taken the bull by the horns", and Botallack was now looking far better.[5]

A feature of the May account was the large sum (£843) spent on coal "owing to a bad cargo and the mine having had to work the steam stamps nearly every Sunday". Tin sold was 138 tons 2 cwt., for £7,331, and arsenic £212 11s. A loss of £19 7s. was sustained, tin having dropped slightly in price again. Higher Mine re-entered the picture with this report. A winze had been sunk from shallow to deep adit on the Bussa in ground that would work at half tribute. The end W. of shallow adit was opening similar ground. In asking for a call of 3s., Capt. James stated that Lord Falmouth had been giving up dues at the rate of £300 for the quarter, "and you ought to back that up by making a similar call".

Matters looked much the same at the September account. Tin sales were down (113 tons 18 cwt.) but about 130 tons had been returned. The loss amounted to

£239 16s., but this was more than accounted for by an item of £381 4s. for a new stamps' axle and flywheel. At Carnyorth, fork and plat had been cut at the 214, and the sinking of Nineveh Shaft would be resumed in a few days. The 214 E. had been driven 20 fathoms, lode not so productive as in the level above, but the 214 W. was opening ground worth £14 per fathom. The 170 W. was being driven under contract by rock drill to communicate with Wheal Cock. This driving with rock drill was rather more expensive, but speed was essential to improve ventilation. The end, moreover, was being driven through a piece of virgin ground; the lode was large and at times had been very productive. In fact, the ground driven through in the last 16 weeks would nearly all work at a profit. About 60 fathoms remained to drive. Another skip road was to be fixed to Nineveh Shaft. At Wheal Cock the 196 was being driven S. towards Skip Shaft. A cross-cut was driving by rock drill at the 112 N. to communicate with a winze sunk under the 100. The 112 had been driven by rock drill about eleven years before, and was very productive for nearly 100 fathoms. About 50 fathoms from the present end it became poor, the main part of the lode having apparently been missed. Men were now opening in the E. wall, and indications were that the lode was probably still there. They had 103 men and boys opening, and 119 stoping ground. During the quarter, the steam stamps' axles had been replaced with four new cam axles, and a new fly wheel fixed. The stamps were now most satisfactory, and provided sufficient stamping power for all stuff that could be raised through the present shaft. A call of 2s. 6d. was made.

A loss of £732 4s. was recorded in December. The labour costs were heavier than usual because they had charged in the wages for building a new stack. Nineveh Shaft had been sunk 13 fathoms under the 214 and was without mineral till the last few feet when a vein had dropped in on the hanging wall, producing rich tinstuff. The 170 W . was still being driven with rock drills towards Wheal Cock, and it was hoped the two mines would be communicated before another sixteen weeks. The lode in this end, with the exception of a few fathoms, had been large, containing arsenic and tin, but not sufficient to pay. Nineveh Shaft was ready for the second skip road; the bottom of the mine, however, had proved so disappointing that it had been decided to postpone its fixing. At Wheal Cock, the ground in the 190 S. towards Skip Shaft being very hard and without mineral, they had stopped driving there, and put the men to sink Skip Shaft. The 150 E. was driving; there were two lodes in the end whose anticipated junction would, it was hoped, make good tin ground. The ends at deep and shallow adits on Bussa lode in Higher Mine were driving, and continued to open ground which worked at half-tribute. 7,277 tons of stuff had been raised and sampled, producing barely 36 lbs. of tin to the ton. Both the quantity and quality raised were disappointing, the former owing to a series of petty mishaps, and the latter to the falling off in the stopes at Nineveh. Some discussion arose as to whether the mine should be kept on, and whether the ticketing system should be adopted for tin sales. It was decided to persevere, limiting expenditure as far as possible, and to defer the ticketing question until the following meeting. A call of 7s. was made to reduce the deficit against the mine.

The loss announced in April 1891, amounted to £1,004. Mr. James regretted the unfavourable statement of accounts, which was due in a great measure to the openings which were large proportionately to the ground being stoped. The cost of driving ends to communicate the two mines had been £550 during the quarter, the ground having increased in hardness. The price of tin had fallen £4 a ton. Owing to the snowstorm—the great March blizzard of 1891—all surface operations had been stopped for a week. But for this, another six tons of tin would have been sold. Another call of 7s. was agreed to. Answering questions, the Purser admitted that the piece of ground between Wheal Cock and Nineveh, which had been considered a good speculation, had produced nothing of value, though there had been "some nice bits here and there". They could not develop the mine in depth without means of sending the men down to their work. A perpendicular shaft had been suggested, but that would cost about £10,000. If such a shaft were not sunk, the mine must eventually cease to work, though it might linger on for a quarter of a century, "but if it is worth being worked at all, let us work it properly and put down a shaft". Mr. John Holman pointed out that the men now worked only four hours per day, owing to the time taken in going to and from their work. If the vertical shaft were sunk, he believed they would get six hours per day out of them. It was eventually agreed to convene a special meeting at Penzance to consider this question.[6]

The loss for August amounted to £319. At Nineveh, the 230 E. was driving in ground that would pay to stope. The winze under the 214 was down to the 230, 7 fathoms in advance of the end, and in similar ground to the end. The 204 E. was driving to prove the ground between Nineveh and Carnyorth 106 fathoms deeper than it had been proved by any other level. The 204 W. was driving in a large lode, but without tin to pay. They were daily expecting to effect communication between this part of the mine at the 170 fathom level and Wheal Cock. Wheal Cock Skip Shaft had been sunk to the 190, skip road fixed, and the men were now driving N. in a lode worth £5 per fathom towards Engine Shaft. In Higher Mine, the ends on Bussa lode at deep and shallow adits were worth £5 per fathom. 6,430 tons of tinstuff had been raised, sampled and stamped in 16 weeks, producing barely 37½ lbs. of tin per ton. At Nineveh, the ground had turned out disappointing, whilst the bottom of Wheal Cock continued to produce a large quantity of low grade tinstuff, but at a slight profit. The S. part towards Higher Mine was turning out satisfactorily. Due to the great exodus of miners to foreign countries during the past few months, leaving them short-handed, the manager had been compelled to stop a few openings. The Chairman also mentioned that their coal cost 17s. 6d. a ton on the mine, but it was delivered at Penzance for 12s. 6d. The meeting agreed to a call of 5s. per share. Concerning the proposal to convene a special meeting to consider the sinking of a new shaft, the Chairman stated that they had recently lost such a large proportion of their men through emigration, that after consulting some of the major shareholders, it was thought better to postpone the matter for a while to see how many men would leave. He thought the shaft could be sunk in about three years. They now had difficulty in getting men to go to the bottom of the mine—"it is simply murder to keep men there".[7]

The loss for December was £118 4s. The openings at Nineveh were reported to have been very unsatisfactory during the past six months, and the returns of tin had fallen off considerably. At Wheal Cock "the 112 has been driving in a large lode containing yellow mundic but no tin. An E. and W. lode has just been intersected which I hope will improve it. This end is being driven in virgin ground under the sea on what has been one of the most productive lodes worked in this mine, viz., Corpus Christi". Men had been opening on the deposit of mineral ground at the 170 and 180 fathom levels, where a large quantity of tinstuff was accumulating. With their present means of hauling this could not be brought to surface. There were 78 men and boys opening ground, and 100 men and boys stoping. In 16 weeks, 6,173 tons of stuff had produced only $28^3/_4$ lbs. of tin per ton—a very striking falling-off, indeed.

It appears that at a special meeting of the adventurers held on August 29th it was decided to ask Capt. W. Rich of Redruth, and Mr. R. H. Williams, of St. Austell, to inspect the mine, and report on the feasibility of the new perpendicular shaft. Their individual findings were laid before the present meeting, Capt. Rich's being to this effect: The chief operations were at Wheal Cock, where there were two shafts, the engine and the skip, the former 25 fathoms N. of the latter. Large quantities of moderately rich tinstone were encountered in the deeper levels; they had been worked to a width of 60 feet, and the quality seemed to be improving in depth. The shafts were sunk to a depth of 190 fathoms below sea level; the climbing was most exhausting to the men, who should be drawn to surface by mechanical means. To sink a new shaft would take much time and money. A skip-road, suitable for skip or cage, could be fixed in the engine shaft without much alteration, and at comparatively small cost . . . He estimated the whole cost of cutting down the shaft, fixing skip-road, and purchasing the engine at not more than £1,300. Everything should be completed in six months. Mr. Williams' recommendations were similar. Wheal Cock engine shaft was 190 fathoms below adit, and the adit giving 25 fathoms more depth, made the whole depth from surface 215 fathoms. It was originally for pumping and winding; but was now used for pumping and a footway for the miners. There was no other shaft in this part of the mine which could be adapted for raising and lowering men, or for increasing the output of ore. The shaft must be enlarged and straightened, from a point about 18 fathoms below surface to the adit, some seven fathoms in length. Then for a considerable depth there were places where irregularities must be remedied by careful blasting to prevent injury to the pitwork. This same road could be used between the relief hours as a skip-road for bringing up tinstuff. A new steam whim would be necessary, and he recommended a modern pair of cylinder engines for the purpose. "At the 190 and 170 fathom levels a large mineral deposit was come upon, and there is every reason to say that this great deposit or Carbona is the result of the junctions of several lodes. At the 180 fathom level some very extensive operations are going on, and large quantities of tinstuff being obtained. This applies also to the 190, and it is reasonable to expect that immense quantities of tinstuff will be obtained from this great Carbona; the value is from 28 to 30 lbs. of tin to the ton; this value I had from the agents. A feature of great importance relating to this mineral deposit is that the junction of the lodes falls S. towards the granite, the granite dipping N. By sinking Wheal Cock shaft 40 or 50 fathoms in a straight line on the course of the lode, the junction of this Carbona and the granite can be opened on and no doubt a very great discovery of tin will be made. The lodes worked on are all richer in this part of the mine in the granite than they are in the green stone. A long level at the 112, extended quite 200 fathoms N. and some 100 fathoms out under the sea, shows in the present end a change, and probably a cross or E. and W. lode will be shortly intersected. A lode out there would be entirely in new ground, and might result in the opening out of a new mine." He thought that the sinking of a new perpendicular shaft could be carried out after rich discoveries had been made. "If the work I have set out be completed, looking to the fact that there is a deep mine almost without water to pump, it will be similar to working a mine above the adit."

Both these reports were adopted, and the manager was instructed to carry out the work forthwith. The March 1892 account included the following items: Henderson and Son, dialling, £40 18s.; Capts. Rich and Williams, inspecting, £12 12s.; labour cost preparing and fixing skip road to Wheal Cock Engine Shaft, £121 6s.; timber, screw bolts, and augers for do., £146 19s. The 16 weeks' loss amounted to £750 4s., a call of 5s. being made. The Chairman said that by next account they would be able to send the men down to the 112 by the new skip road. At Nineveh, the 230 E. was driving, and had been opening stoping ground, but was now poor. There was a large lode in the 214 E. The tin ground gone down under the 204 should shortly be reached. At Wheal Cock, the 190 N. was driving in a large lode, but stuff of too low quality to work. The 180 N. was driving in a lode 3 feet wide, rich for arsenic, and worth £7 per fathom for tin. The lode intersected in the 180 S. had been driven on eastward for 9 fathoms in the granite, but being poor, they had just commenced to drive on it westwards in the killas. Since communication had been effected between Nineveh and Wheal Cock the ventilation of both mines had much improved. There were 74 men and boys opening, and 134 men and boys stoping. 6,851 tons of tinstuff had produced 33½ lbs. of tin per ton. Wheal Cock Engine Shaft had been cut down and dividers fixed to the 100 fathoms level. The men were now fixing runners. A pair of second-hand 20 inch cylinder winding engines, with drums and brake gear, had been purchased at a cost of about £400. Now that fine weather could be expected, the building of engine- and boiler houses, and surface erections in connection with the skip road would be commenced.[8]

On June 30th, it was reported that fires had been lighted in the new engine by which means the men were to be lowered and raised in Wheal Cock, and it was expected that in a short time all the machinery would be in operation. The July account read: labour, £4,342 7s.; merchants, £1,529 1s.; miscellaneous, £128 12s.; skip road in Wheal Cock, £1,385 17s.; total expenditure, £7,385 19s. 113 tons 10 cwt. of tin realised £6,174 8s.; 46 tons 8 cwt. of arsenic, £232; total £6,406 9s. Debit balance, £979 9s.; total balance against the mine, £1,578 11s. A lode had been intersected in the 135 S. which appeared to be the Corpus Christi; this was worth £14 per fathom for 10 fathoms. The skip road in Wheal Cock Engine Shaft had been completed to the 100 fathom level.

A call of 10s. was made at the November meeting. Mr. James expressed himself sanguine of future success, adding that the mine was raising more stuff now than ever before, though the produce was 10 lbs. less than formerly. The February account of 1893 disclosed a quarter's loss of £793 9s. 7d., requiring a further call of 10s. The Purser stated that "a great many shares had been relinquished", and it was decided to call a special meeting on March 15th to declare forfeit all shares on which calls were in arrear. The question of insuring the miners was discussed. Mr. James said they had tried insurance at Botallack some years ago, the arrangement being that a lump sum should be paid in case of death, and so much for a certain time in case of injury. At present, if a man were injured, he got 5s. per week from the mine club, and that payment went on until the mine stopped or the funds were exhausted.—Mr. Olds: "That is the worst feature of it. When the mine stops the poor fellow's pay stops". It was decided to consider this matter at the special meeting. The agents reported the 230 E. at Nineveh hard and poor. The lode in the 214 E. became poor shortly after last meeting, its character being similar to that in the level above which had been driven 40 fathoms further E. than this end and poor all the distance. It had been stopped, and the men were driving on a lode S. of E. about 30 fathoms behind. The end was in fairly easy ground, worth £4 per fathom. At Wheal Cock the 190 and 180 N. had been communicated, and opened ground working at 8s. tribute. The 180 N. on Tolven was similarly valued. The 160 S. had intersected a cross-course on which the end was being driven E. to meet the Corpus Christi. The 150, 135, and 125 were being driven S. on Corpus Christi, but though producing tin were scarcely good enough to work. The skip-road was complete to the 135 fathom level. Men had been engaged sinking a shaft, driving a level and fixing pitwork at the steam stamps— the old shaft and level through which the stamps water was pumped up having collapsed. This had entailed an expenditure of £300. besides an increased consumption of coal through having to keep an engine pumping water from the adit for tin-dressing purposes. The skip-road would now again be proceeded with.

Tinstuff raised and stamped in the quarter amounted to 8,323 tons, producing 32 lbs. of tin per ton. The Purser stated they had now enough ground open to keep them working for 20 years to come. He expressed sympathy with the sad accident which had closed down their nearest neighbour, Wheal Owles—a reference to the mundation there when twenty miners lost their lives.

In the June quarter, 138 tons 7 cwt. of tin were sold for £6,993 4s., which with arsenic sales, £150, made the total credits £7,143 4s. A profit of £15 9s. had been made, the total adverse balance being £1,448 16s. Mr. James stated that the skip road would be completed to the 170 within a fortnight and as soon as it was completed to the 180, more stuff could be brought up. New pumping gear at stamps had cost £71 5s.; excavating and labour for new buddles, £74 1s.; repairs to engine and boilers and insurance, £144 17s.; Skip Shaft at Wheal Cock, £179 12s. The Purser said the work of overhauling and inspecting the boilers had cost a good bit of money, but there was no fear now in regard to them. There were no better boilers in the county than those at Botallack, and only two as good. Mr. Peter Olds (one of the great "characters" among the shareholders) was not happy at the way in which the mine was being run. He would like to see their adverse balance all paid off, so that they might start "fair and fitty" and manage their business like other businesses were managed. The fact of the matter was they were paying out and did not know what they were paying it for.—The Purser: Oh, yes, we do.—Mr. Peter Olds: Well, I don't. (A laugh.) Nobody knows what we are paying for and it seems to me, nobody cares . . . I have studied the mine for the last 30 years, and I can't make it out. If the thing won't pay to work on her bottom, shut her up. If you cannot manage to keep enough money in reserve to pay the men, I say "Shut up the mine". We are paying between £300 and £400 in interest and commission. It is a nuisance to me, but it is like all the rest of mines. They are all conducted the same way. (A laugh.)—The Purser (consulting the bank book): Mr. Peter Olds makes rather rash statements, for we have only paid £150 in the past twelve months for interest and commission.—Peter Olds thereupon withdrew this part of his allegation; but he probably displayed a sounder grasp of the mine's financial affairs in this exchange than the Purser. Living "on tick" seems to have been a besetting sin of cost-book companies at that period. He later wrung from the Purser an admission that a further bank charge of £60 was required in connection with a surface erection at Wheal Cock.—Mr. Peter Olds: You muddle things up so. The charges for the year are some thing like £200, so I was not very wide of the mark.—The Purser: They will not be very much in the future—Mr. Peter Olds: I would rather see the balance paid off now, and then work the mine on our own capital.—The Purser: You express the opinion of everyone connected with the mine, when you say that.—Mr. Peter Olds: Well, that is all I meant. (A laugh.)—The Purser: That is all right.

The adventurers agreed to a call of 5s. The agents reported the 230 and 214 ends driving S. at Nineveh on a lode E. of shaft, worth £6 per fathom. The 204 E.

on Nogger was poor. They were driving the 204 W. with rock drill to communicate to the winze sinking under the 170 W.; this should be done within the next two months, when a large section of ground would be available for stoping. At Wheal Cock, the 180 N. had been opening tribute ground. The 160 was being driven E. on a cross-course to intersect Corpus Christi. In the 112 N. the junction of the two lodes did no good, but the end was being continued in easy ground. Skip road in Engine Shaft would be completed to the 170 within a fortnight. As soon as it was completed to the 180, additional stuff could be brought up; but with present winding appliances no more could be done, so the sinking and opening up of the bottom of the mine had to be temporarily suspended. 72 men and boys were opening, and 101 stoping ground. Commenting on this report, Mr. James said they were not sure what lode it was they had at the E. of shaft, but thought it was the Chycornish lode. At least, it was very similar in character. They knew it for the present as the South lode. There was some tin in the 204 E. in Nineveh; while the Corpus Christi, in Wheal Cock, where they met with some mineral N. and S., must now form a junction with some other lode before it would "make" mineral again. They were expecting to communicate the 112 with it. The intersection of the granite occurred at the bottom of Wheal Cock Skip Shaft. They were thinking of installing additional plant to prevent "the loss of tin going away over cliff". Speaking later at the dinner, he remarked that if they had known how things were going to turn out they would perhaps have stopped the mine. But they could not see what the produce of their stuff would be, nor rule in any way the price of tin. What they had done was to put in apparatus for raising the stuff as economically as possible. Ald. Chenhalls said it had been his good fortune to sit under the pursership of Mr. James' grandfather and father, and he did not think the present manager lost anything by comparison with his predecessors. Mr. James had to work the mine under adverse circumstances, and he had done so with pluck—the obstinate pluck of a Cornishman.[9]

At the October meeting, the accounts showed: labour, £3,790 5s., of which £1,133 6s. was paid for tribute; merchants, £1,596 5s.; labour and materials for skip shaft at Wheal Cock, £345 3s.; engines and boilers, repairs and sundries, £132 13s.; excavating for new tin leavings, £59; bank charges, £50; stamps' rents, £55; Stannary assessment, £5 17s.; carriage of tin, £29 19s.; total, £6,064 4s. Black tin sold (108 tons 17 cwt.) £4,890; arsenic, £249 6s.; showing a loss on the four months of £924 18s. Nineveh Shaft was sinking under the 203, ground poor; but there was a good piece of tin ground gone down under the 230 E. The 230 and 214 ends driving S., E. of shaft, were poor. The 204 W. had been communicated to the winze sunk under the 170, ground opened of too low quality to work at a profit. The 204 E. was driving in a large lode, ground easy. This part of the mine had proved very disappointing for some time past. The new Skip or Engine Shaft at Wheal Cock had been sunk from 170 to 180, and was being continued to the 190 level (the bottom of this part of the mine). The manager's object here was to continue sinking with all speed on the Tolven lode, which dipped W., to cut the Crowns lode, which dipped E. This should take place in about 70 fathoms below the 190, the Crowns being the lode which had produced such rich deposits of copper and tin many years before. The 160 cross-cut E. was being driven by rock drill. The 135 E. on Corpus Christi was worth £4 per fathom, and looked more promising than for the past 20 fathoms. A rise over the 125 S. had been communicated to the 112, opening up what was hoped would be a large section of profitable ground. The surface erections for the new skip road were about complete, and in another month this shaft would be available for winding stuff, by which time it would have cost nearly £3,000. The manager had contracted two months previously for the erection of frames, etc., for the tin leavings; the cost of this would come into the next account. Sufficient tin should be saved in twelve months to pay all outlay and working expenses. The loss shown this quarter was disheartening, but the continuing low price of tin, with the noncessation of exploratory work, accounted for it. There were 8 tons of low grade stuff and roughs at water stamps unstamped; if returned, this would reduce the loss to about £600. Answering queries, Mr. James explained that the £59 spent on the new tin leavings had been for excavating, masons' labour, etc. There would be five revolving frames altogether. The work was to have been finished by September 29th, "but they are not the most expeditious workmen going". They hoped now to get fairly started by November 1st.—Mr. R. Thomas: You hope to see the same returns by the next meeting?—The Purser: We return here on an average 110 tons a quarter, 16 weeks. On the Red River, where the mines in the past few years have put in some tin saving appliances, they save about 10 per cent on the tin that the mine returns. The streamers used to save 25 per cent. In Botallack we shall save about 11 tons on our present 16 weeks' returns, of the value of £400. Less than £400 will pay for the whole of the work we want, so that I think the expenditure is quite justifiable.—Later, speaking of the rise put in to connect the 112 with the 125 in Wheal Cock, Mr. James stated that "we have a lode there six or seven feet wide on the average; we calculate it is 30 fathoms long and we know it is 30 fathoms high, but we cannot touch that ground yet, though it is as good a bit of ground as we have in the mine". This was owing to their lack of hauling power, which would be remedied by the imminent completion of the new Skip Shaft. Nineveh, however, was "abominably poor"; they lost nearly all their money there. They would have to keep the mine open, and he thought it best to keep on sinking the shaft, and a man and a boy in the ends. They would be down to the 190 at Wheal Cock in about six weeks' time; and if they went down in the same sort of lode they would have a bal there good enough for anything; indeed, he should never live to see the end of it.

After a call of 7s. had been agreed, Mr. R. Thomas asked how long they would be sinking the 70 fathoms below the 190, in connection with the development of the Crowns lode. The Purser replied they hoped to have the work done at the latest by June, 1895. He did not expect to be making calls in the meantime. Just after the last meeting there was a wave of emigration from the mine and the parish, the prices (wages) being cut when the price of tin went down. The men left for other mines in the county as well as for S. Africa and America, but many were back again now, and they had ample labour and ample stuff to break. They could take on another 50 men in a fortnight's time, and be glad to have them. If they could get anything like £50 a ton for their tin, they would make a good profit.

The account for January 1894, included charges of £208 8s. for Wheal Cock Skip Shaft, and £218 15s., labour and materials for tin leavings. The balance against the adventurers was £2,566 13s., though unsold tin and arsenic had been valued at £850. A call of 15s. was made. The manager reported Wheal Cock Engine Shaft sunk about 5 fathoms under the 190, lode large and producing tin. From the appearance of the sides, it was judged that the deposit of tin ore being worked on between the 160 and 190 was continuing in depth. An end driving N. of shaft at the 190 was producing good tin stuff. Winzes had been sunk under the 180 and a large quantity of ground opened which was working at 8s. tribute. This part of the mine was being developed with all speed, and a few months would throw great light on its future prospects. At Nineveh, the shaft had been sunk 16 fathoms under the 230; for the first 14 it was poor; the next fathom was worth £15; and at present it was worth £7 per fathom. The winze sinking under the 230 became poor, and the piece of tin ground under this level had been taken away. A month ago Mr. James stopped the driving of the ends; for six months they had been without tin, and in most uncongenial ground—decomposed granite. During the past six years the shaft had been sunk 70 fathoms, and ends extended E. and W. nearly 300 fathoms, yet at the present time about two tons of tin per month was as much as could be raised. The shaft could not be sunk any deeper without a considerable outlay on pitwork. The cost of keeping the mine in order was not less than £80 a month. Taking all these points into consideration, he recommended this part of the mine be abandoned forthwith. At Wheal Cock the new skip road was completed to the 190, and was working most satisfactorily. It had been completely paid for. The tin leavings would shortly be working but he feared that with tin at its present price, cost could not be met in the coming quarter, though the loss should be very little. Forty-five men and boys were opening, and 107 stoping ground on tribute. Tinstuff raised amounted to 8,240 tons, producing $33\frac{1}{2}$ lbs. tin per ton.

In a subsequent discussion, Mr. James mentioned that the previous day a splendid stone of tin had been broken in the shaft being sunk under the 230 in Nineveh. All the other points here had been stopped, as they had got into rotten ground, and were producing nothing. On hearing this, several adventurers expressed the opinion that the manager should continue operations there, at least for a time. Mr. H. Olds remarked that the darkest hour was always before the dawn and on this basis it was decided to leave the matter in the manager's hands, on the understanding that he would call a special meeting to reconsider the question, should that prove necessary.[10]

The figures presented in May were: expenditure, £7,167; credits, £7,020; so that, despite a further great depreciation in tin, the loss was only £146. However, the total adverse balance amounted to £1,439, to reduce which the meeting made a call of 5s. In four months 163 men and boys had opened 110 fathoms of ground and sent to grass 7,960 tons of tinstuff, yielding 40½lbs. of tin per ton.

The September account disclosed a loss of £236, and a call of 5s. was made. 127 tons of tin had been sold for £5,038, at prices varying from £41 10s. to £31 15s. per ton, whilst arsenic was credited at £379. Engine Shaft was sinking below the 210, but the work had been rather impeded by the need to fix new pitwork from the 170 to the 200. At Nineveh, the lode in the 170 W. was large but poor. The deposit of tin ground at Wheal Cock being worked on from the 160 to the 185 had not yet been traced above or below these points, but there still remained a large reserve of this ground. 57 men and boys were opening and 84 stoping ground on tribute. 7,590 tons of stuff had been raised, producing about 37 lbs. of tin per ton. During that month a party of South Wales engineers visited the mine. They found the workings to be 220 fathoms below sea level, and still sinking. The winding and pumping machinery were of modern type, the engines being capable of winding 1½ tons a minute from a depth of a quarter of a mile.

These distinguished visitors, who had the good fortune to see Botallack working in such an efficient manner, and nearly meeting her running expenses despite the ruinously low price of tin, would probably have been incredulous if told that within four months a decision would be taken to close the mine. Yet this was the fate now imminently in store. The first signs of impending disaster came during the middle of November. At that time the whole of west Cornwall was seriously affected by a disastrous cloudburst, this event being preceded by several weeks of heavy rain. As a result, the St. Just mines were seriously flooded. The tin stream works below St. Just at Botallack Bottoms, belonging to the mine, were swept away, whilst the destruction of bridges cut off passage from one side to the other. Surface water came in large quantities into both Levant and Botallack, considerably impeding operations, and certain parts of Wheal Cock were said to have been "struck idle". The full extent of the damage, however, was not revealed until December 21st, in the manager's quarterly report. This described how the water came into Wheal Cock from Nineveh. A substantial dam, consisting of 2 feet of concrete and 3 feet of brickwork, between the two mines, had been left open for the better ventilation of Wheal Cock, causing the latter to be flooded. There was thus no object in retaining Carnyorth sett, and he advised its being surrendered, entailing as it did a cost of between £40 and £50 per month.

However, the general position of the mine had by now deteriorated so alarmingly that the punch-drunk adventurers, who had received no dividend for 22 years, resolved to do more than close one section, and to shut up the whole mine. The account presented for their consideration showed a loss of £653 5s. and a total debit balance of £2,486 11s. The Purser said they commenced the quarter with tin at £40 7s. 6d. a ton and finished at £34 15s.—"that took all the starch out of the tin collar", and he called attention to the enormous quantities of tin coming in from abroad.—Mr. Chenhalls: Fresh lots will come from Western Australia.—Mr. James: No one will bother about tin in Western Australia while they have got gold. It is the enormous production of the Straits and the low price of silver that we have to fear.—Mr. Mason: About 2,500 tons came from the Straits during the last fortnight.—The Purser stated they had spent their average amount (£700) last quarter on driving, rising and sinking, and only the same amount for breaking tin as for opening ground. Tributers had done badly, the produce being now only 29 lbs. to the ton instead of 37 lbs., as at last account. This 8 lbs. difference meant 3s. a ton less on all stuff raised, a total of over £1,000. But for the flood they would have raised 12 tons of tin more, which would have yielded an additional £350. The actual loss in working through the flood was 1,000 tons of tinstuff. There were now 1,748 shares held, and deducting recoverable arrears of calls, the debt to be cleared off was £2,000. It was decided to make a 30s. call.

Giving his report, the manager stated that with the tin price continuing to fall and the produce of their tinstuff so low, he had thought it advisable to curtail openings for a while, and had also lowered wages. The last four weeks of the account had been most unfortunate. Owing to feast holidays, a fire at the dry, and excessive rains flooding the bottom of the mine, the quantity of tinstuff raised had fallen off quite 100 tons; this, with extra cost incurred, accounted for about £600 of the loss. With the prevailing price of tin, he saw no possibility of meeting cost. The adventurers, on his recommendation, then decided to give up Carnyorth sett, thereby saving about £50 a month. The Chairman said that Mr. Bolitho himself and others could see no use in working Botallack with no immediate prospect of a rise in tin. He thought they might continue through the winter out of sympathy with the miners, who would not otherwise get employment. Botallack had cost them £12,000 in the last six years, and might cost another £10-15,000 before the price of tin went up again. "A slight rise would be useless. Botallack can do nothing unless tin is in the nineties." Capt. Oats said he had invested more out of regard for the locality than anything else. Messrs. Bolitho's judgement was that they did not see any prospect of an improvement, yet, like himself, they were reluctant to precipitate a catastrophe. One uninformed shareholder asked if it would take until midsummer to "pick her eyes out", but the purser rejoined there was not an eye in her! Eventually it was decided that, if necessary, the manager would call a special meeting to wind up the mine. They might then leave the machinery as it stood and wait for better times; or sell out. If the mine ever started again, modern machinery would be necessary.

The decision to close the mine at this time was made almost inevitable by the general trend of events. Desperate attempts had been made to stave off disaster: they had been cleaning up the floors for the last six years, and had got 100 tons of tin from the old bottoms which had not been cleaned previously for fifty years: there was not a pitch in the mine which could be worked for 9s. 6d.: the tributers were not making a living, and the men were gradually leaving the mine. Botallack could not go on with tin at £35 a ton.

The decision to close the mine brought cries of anguish from its employees. "Anxious Miner", writing in the *Cornishman* on January 24th 1895, stated that "1,200 mouths depend on the earnings of those who are employed at the mine ... Will it not cause a great calamity to the parish if she's to be shut down?" The promised special meeting of the adventurers took place at Penzance, on January 30th, to consider the advisability or otherwise of suspending operations. Mr. James reported that the produce had improved since their last general meeting, and now averaged nearly 40 lbs. to the ton. If this continued, their loss would not be more than about £150 for the next two months. The working cost was £800 a month, and that of the current quarter would be £3,500. 208 men and boys were employed, 90 underground, with 78 on tribute. Mr. T. R. Bolitho said that he and his cousin were willing to continue operations until the next ordinary meeting, at least; and it was accordingly decided to continue operations for the present, and call a further special meeting if the manager thought it necessary.[11]

It seemed, however, as if the Fates were determined that the mine should not survive. On the afternoon of February 5th, the dam at Wheal Cock that kept the water from the North-fields part of the mine collapsed and the workings were flooded. It had been thought advisable, in order to lessen expenses, to build this weir at Wheal Cock to hold the water and stop the engine working at Northfields, or Nineveh, when that sett had been abandoned some months previously. It was of substantial construction, and though not raised to the top of the adit was sufficiently high to restrain the water and form a reservoir in Nineveh of considerable length. The recent heavy floods greatly augmented this body of water, and believing it must eventually overflow, the management commenced building an outer dam to keep back the surplus water. This had not been completed, however; and so, at about three o'clock, when the water overflowed, the dam burst from pressure upon it, and the liberated flood rushed through the level to join the water which had for some time stood in the bottom of Wheal Cock. This filled the shaft to the 112 fathom level; and as the antiquated engines were unable to cope with this new burden, the suspension of Wheal Cock followed automatically. This would probably have happened within a few months, in any case, as only the best bit of ground there had been worked recently (to keep the men employed during the winter)—thus accounting for the improvement in produce which Mr. James had reported to the special meeting.

THE ROAD TO RUIN

Fortunately, the accident, while expediting the discharge of the men, did not involve any loss of life. It occurred when the men were changing cores, and only 20 or 30 were underground, these being 50 fathoms or more from the dam when the water came away. Some, however, had been working below the 112, so their escape was indeed a providential one.

The results of this accident were soon made apparent. On February 14th it was reported that another batch of surface men—nearly 20—had been discharged. The news that all dreaded to hear came on March 18th, when all the men employed at Botallack had notice that their services were to be dispensed with in a few days. It was not thought likely that Levant would undertake to work a part of the mine, as she was only doing moderately well herself, and Botallack levels were a long distance from Levant's present workings. Capt. F. Oats (who was then abroad) offered to take 5,000 shares if the mine were re-started in 50,000 or 100,000 shares, but the other large shareholders did not approve of such a large outlay on a doubtful concern.

At a meeting of the adventurers held at Chyandour on March 21st, Arthur James announced there had been no response to advertisements offering the mine for sale as a going concern, and the only thing to do now was to sell the machinery and materials piece-meal. He estimated their value at £2,000. He said the men would cease working on the Saturday following, but it would take a week or ten days more to clean up the floors and return the last parcel of tin. There were now 127 men and boys employed. During the past month 50 men had been discharged, most of whom had been taken on at Levant. Materials cost about £250 and labour £450 per month, and on the closing two months' working there would be a loss of about £1,200. They had offered the men on tribute 15s. in the £ to encourage them and the mine had been carried on more as a charitable than a commercial concern. It was agreed to invite tenders from wreckers and dismantlers, but to offer to allow the engine on Wheal Cock to remain should Lord Falmouth desire it so that it might be used if the mine were resumed at a future date. Mr. Bolitho remarked that when they found a lord who treated the adventurers so liberally they might well acknowledge it by showing him any little act of courtesy. A remarkable statement made at this meeting came from A. H. James, the chairman, who declared, in reply to a question, that he believed Botallack *had been worked for seven hundred years*. It would be interesting to know the printed source from which he claimed to have derived this information.[12]

On June 6th, the *Cornish Telegraph* carried an advertisement stating that "Mr. Barnes Richards has received instructions from the Purser and adventurers in the Botallack mine to sell by Auction on the Mine, on Tuesday June 18th, commencing at 12 o'clock (noon) prompt, a large quantity of Materials." These consisted principally of timber, wooden and galvanised iron shedding, wire rope, chains, several water wheels, 4 feet to 12 feet diameter, five 16 foot revolving convex frames (nearly new), about 100 dead frames, 20 round buddles, tin kieves, and hutches. In such fashion the pathetic remains of the once mighty Botallack were broken up, scattered and dispersed, whilst underground the unchecked waters steadily rose and drowned the workings where generations of miners had laboured to win the rich deposits of tin and copper.

1 *Cornish Telegraph*, February 28th 1884.
2 *Cornish Telegraph*, May 27th 1886.
3 *Cornish Telegraph*, December 1st 1887.
4 *Cornish Telegraph*, October 10th 1889.
5 *Cornish Telegraph*, January 30th 1890.
6 *Cornish Telegraph*, April 23rd 1891.
7 *Cornish Telegraph*, August 13th 1891.
8 *Cornish Telegraph*, March 24th 1892.
9 *Cornish Telegraph*, June 15th 1893.
10 *Cornish Telegraph*, January 25th 1894.
11 *Cornishman*, January 31st 1895.
12 *Cornish Telegraph*, March 28th 1895.

23. Stamps and mill buildings. (1907)

24. Botallack - the surface remains. (1985)

Chapter Seven:
An Unsuccessful Revival

Many other mines, besides Botallack, were crushed out of existence at this time by the prevailing adverse economic circumstances. Very few of the hundreds which had flourished in the county during the middle years of the century survived at its close. However, around 1906 a welcome advance in metal prices, coupled with the introduction of new and more efficient mining machinery, led to a modest revival in the industry, one of the mines selected for renewed attention being Botallack. A limited liability company, The Cornish Consolidated Tin Mines, Ltd., acquired a lease of the sett, its capital consisting of 150,000 shares of £1 each. The directors were Francis Allen (Chairman of Clitters United Mines, Ltd., Gunnislake); Sir Lewis William Molesworth, Grampound Road; George Hill Dunsmure, London; General Sir Reginald Pole Carew; and Harry John Meyerstein, Chevening, Kent (a director of South Crofty Ltd.). The manager was William Thomas, the head office being in London.

Its prospectus, dated November 7th 1906, showed that the company had acquired the setts of Botallack (about 200 acres), Carnyorth (about 150), and Buzza or Truthwall (about 200), the combined properties covering an area of nearly one square mile. "The lodes on these properties" it was stated, "have been profitably worked for tin and copper throughout a long period, although little is known of the results previous to 1802, whilst from that date to 1836 Botallack was worked only in a small way by five adventurers, who are stated to have divided £34,000 as profits. From 1836 the records of the Cost Book company show that:

Ores sold from Botallack from 1836-95 were:

Tin ores, value	£829,664
Copper ores, value	220,701
Arsenical ores, value	6,481
Total	£1,056,846

The total does not include sales of Carnyorth or Buzza mineral, which also realised several hundred thousand pounds sterling."

The result of working Botallack for tin for the last five years prior to suspension (1890-4 inclusive) was: black tin sold in five years: 1,880 tons for £92,270. The average selling price was £49, compared with the current (1906) price of about £120. The prospectus gave the reasons for closing Botallack at the end of 1895 as the low price ruling for tin, and the limitations of the cost book

113

system with its attendant lack of working capital. "For the last five years of the Cost Book Company's existence it had been producing black tin at a cost of £55 and selling it at an average of £49, every ton being produced at a loss of £6. Had it been working during the five years 1900-05 inclusive, its average profit on tin alone, and that in spite of antiquated and wasteful methods, would have been £18 per ton, whilst were the old Company working today, with the present price of black tin, its gross profits would be over £60 on every ton sold and that without taking any account of copper or arsenic values. In other words, with its then restricted annual output of 376 tons, Botallack might now be realising a profit of over £22,000 per annum, from tin alone."

The prospectus went on to castigate the wasteful methods of the Cost Book Company, adducing as proof of this the fact that since the closing down of the mine in 1895 tin stuff carted from the dumps to water stamps and dressed by primitive methods had been sold for about £30,000, whilst thousands of tons awaited treatment by the new Company as soon as the unwatering of the mine was commenced. The depth of Botallack was not much over half that of Levant, its wealthy neighbour. "In this connection it is interesting to note that the Crowns and Wheal Cock lodes—the richest worked by the old Botallack and Carnyorth Company—have opposite underlies, or … are dipping towards each other. It is calculated from the dip that these two lodes will intersect one another 30 fathoms below the present bottom of the mine … Throughout Cornwall, similar junctions of productive lodes have invariably yielded rich deposits of tin and copper."

During the last five years of working, the old Cost Book company achieved an average recovery rate of 36 lbs. per ton of tinstuff treated. Under the methods then used, it was reasonable to assume that the ore stuff so treated averaged quite 45 lbs., the loss of black tin being then 25-30 per cent of the actual lode contents. The new company hope to obtain a recovery of not less than 40 lbs., equal to a recovery rate of over £2 per ton of stuff treated, quite apart from copper and arsenic values. Working costs had equalled about £1 per ton of stuff milled; these could be reduced to 17s. 6d. by the use of modern methods. Electric power would be provided for the mine from a central station. It was proposed to erect a 60-head Californian stamp battery in 20-head sections, each head having a crushing capacity of 3 tons per day. 20 heads would be erected for working the dumps; a further 20 would follow the unwatering of the mine; and the third section of 20 as development advanced. The full 60 head could treat 180 tons of stuff per day, or 54,000 tons per year. With black tin recovery at not less than 40s. value and costs not exceeding 17s. 6d. per ton, the working profit was calculated at 22s. 6d., or £60,000 a year

From 1836-95 copper ores sold represented over 20 per cent of the value of the mine's production at a time when the dressing of Cornish copper ores received but scant attention. The upper levels of Botallack were believed still to contain large reserves of this ore, but no account had been taken of these in calculating these future profits. Copper recovery and dressing would, however, be made a special feature, its value then being over £90 a ton.

Leases for 21 years from September 29th had been obtained at annual minimum rents totalling £293, which merged in a royalty of $^1/_{25}$th on all minerals when the price of black tin exceeded £80 per ton and $^1/_{30}$th when below that price.

The first meeting of the Company[1] took place in February 1907. Francis Allen (Chairman) described how they had started by putting in order the dilapidated count-house and other existing buildings, put the carpenters' shop to work, and were erecting saw mills, a dry and other necessary structures. Orders had been placed for the electrical and dressing plant. They would not have to wait until the mine was drained to commence milling, as there was already a dump of fair value on the ground, whilst they could also draw a considerable amount of minerals from the upper levels as the water level was lowered. During the summer of 1905, which was very dry, the water in the mine fell some feet, and the tributers were then able to get into Nineveh adit and break 300 tons, their recovery being 44 lbs. per ton,—rather high, having regard to the primitive conditions. About fifty masons, carpenters and surface miners were so far employed. An acre of ground had been acquired near the mine to build a house for the manager, who then lived at St. Just.

By the lease granted by Lord Falmouth they were under covenant to begin a new central shaft within two years. This would, in fact, be commenced in March, and take two or three years to sink. He thought if they averaged nine feet of sinking per week they would be doing well. Meanwhile, a masonry collar had been put around Wheal Cock Shaft, and preparations made to bring it into active use again. They were also clearing the adit level, which appeared to be choked some 50 fathoms in. They did not propose afterwards to use that adit for draining, as all water would be lifted to surface for dressing, but for draining for the time being it would be worth while to clear it as far as they could. As electric pumps would be used, it was thought that pumping would take place in two or three shafts simultaneously.

In a report issued in July, William Thomas, the manager, described the work carried out up to the end of June 1907, which may be summarised as follows:

Botallack: Main adit cleared and re-timbered for 130 fathoms from outfall at sea level, and enlarged to admit the use of a tram waggon. The men were now between Narrow and Botallack Shafts, approaching the killas-granite junction. The last 50 fathoms cleared in the killas had been through absolute chokage, and considerable quantities of timber had been required. Wheal Hazard adit had been cleared from outfall to Wheal Hazard Shaft, and thence about 30 fathoms beyond.

Wheal Cock: A new 20 foot collar had been built around Skip Shaft. Engine Shaft had been re-collared in concrete 40 feet in height and shaft cleared to adit (40 fathoms), the shaft now being ready for the first electric pump. Wheal Cock adit had been cleared from outfall at sea level to both Engine and Skip Shafts, and 100 fathoms beyond these shafts towards Nineveh. To reach the adit outfall a ladder road of 260 feet was constructed down the face of the cliff.

Nineveh Shaft had been re-opened and timbered 40 fathoms from surface, or to within 4 fathoms of the water, and was now ready for the second electric pump. Tolvan adit had been completely cleared.

Carnyorth: Lobby Shaft had been cleared to water level at this point, 25 fathoms from surface, and a choke in the adit was being cleared.

On the surface, a new block of buildings, comprising smiths' shop, fitting shop, traction-engine house, sawmill and men's dinner house had been completed, also a new weighbridge house and general stores. The former Company's offices had been repaired and now included a drawing office and chemical laboratory, whilst the old stables had been converted into a carpenters' shop. Accommodation had been provided for the Penzance School of Mines, in place of their former tenancy of the count house. The power station for accommodating gas engines and dynamos was ready for the roof. This building measured 61 feet x 31 feet and would contain four gas engines capable of developing 800 h.p. The site for 40 heads of Californian stamps had been cleared, and half the number of heads had already been delivered on the mine. The sites for new winding engines and boiler house, as well as for the new shaft, had been cleared. A yard had been taken at Penzance from the Corporation where stores could be lodged. A traction engine had been purchased to facilitate the removal of supplies from Penzance station and quays to the mine. In carrying out repairs to shaft and adit they had found, especially at Nineveh, considerable quantities of low grade but payable ore, standing above water level. About 180 hands were engaged, including 60 underground.

During the winter of 1907-8 a sharp division of opinion, amounting to a crisis, arose between the directors on the one hand, and William Thomas, the manager, on the other, regarding the manner in which the mine should be worked. It appears that a mistake was made by Lord Falmouth, when granting the lease, in making it conditional on the sinking of a new vertical central shaft. A new shaft was, indeed, essential for reworking the mine, but it was considered it should not have been sited where it was, in the inland part which had been virtually unbottomed and worked out by the old nineteenth century company, but away out under the sea, as a diagonal shaft, and on the rich Wheal Cock lodes rather than those of the Crowns. Though inevitably committed to the central (Allen's) shaft scheme, William Thomas was nevertheless fully aware of the potential of the submarine section, and his original plan included the unwatering of Wheal Cock as one of its essential features. Meanwhile, however, the directors had become infatuated with the Allen's Shaft project, which was conceived and executed on a grandiose scale—principally, so it is alleged, as a market counter for share dealing. As their views were now running counter to those of their manager, Mr. W. R. Thomas was brought in as his successor to ensure that Allen's Shaft was sunk quickly. On taking over, however, W. R. Thomas realised the mistake that had been made, and slowed down the sinking of Allen's. This, again, displeased the directors, and he in turn was replaced as manager by Mr. Climas to expedite the sinking.

At the first ordinary general meeting of the Company, held in June 1908, it was stated that during the year they had cleared a mile and a third of adits, opened four of the old shafts, and commenced a new one. Including the sinking of the new shaft, a quarter of a mile of shaft work had been dealt with. This new shaft was down 50 fathoms, the timber being put in as fast as it was sunk, and the cage road in it, so that it would be available for hoisting as soon as required. They originally intended to install in the power house three engines of 150 h.p. each, but realising these would hardly suffice, a unit of 315 h.p. was substituted in place of the third one of 150 h.p. There had been delay in delivering this plant, and subsequently a breakdown in the gas producers. However, everything was now working satisfactorily. Pumping commenced in February in Wheal Cock, and the electric pump had no difficulty in lowering the water to the 33 fathom level, at which point it was stopped, because the water in Nineveh, which backs against Carnyorth, was not lowering at all. It was apparent that there existed a certain amount of danger in going too far in either direction until the water was correspondingly lowered in the adjoining section, as otherwise the dams separating them might give way under pressure. The Nineveh pump was almost ready to start, and as soon as the water there had been lowered to the same level as in Wheal Cock, the two sections would be drained concurrently. Twenty head of stamps had been erected, and the dressing plant all installed; it would commence work within a week, so they hoped to appear in the ticketings at the end of July.

Because of the ease with which the coastal mines could be unwatered, the company had applied for the Wheal Owles sett, and with the exception of one owner, all the lords had agreed to grant them a lease. For this, they would pay £160 per annum when not making use of the property, and undertake to unwater it within two years.[2] The mine could be worked with their own electrical plant, by means of a power line. (This scheme never fully materialised.)

The new manager described their property as comprising Botallack, with Buzza, Parknoweth, Chycornish and Crowns. The first four of these were interconnected at the 100 fathom level below adit, whilst the fifth was connected with them at the 80. These all lay S. of Allen's Shaft, whilst to the N. of it lay the group comprising Wheal Cock, Nineveh and Carnyorth. Nineveh and Wheal

Cock were holed together at the 112 below adit; at which level dams prevented water from draining from one part to the other. After both mines had been drained concurrently to this depth, the dams would be destroyed, and one set of pumps would then suffice for unwatering the two sections. The unwatering of the group would be carried out from Allen's Shaft as soon as this had been sunk 900 feet from surface. The incoming water from the whole area, which in the past had been dealt with by a large number of pumping engines fixed in small and crooked shafts, was extremely light, and when once centralised would be easily and economically handled.

At Nineveh, a new tramway had just commenced delivering ore to the battery. Allen's Shaft having reached deep adit level, the men were opening out stations on each side of the shaft, on completion of which cross-cutting would immediately be started. The erection of a new winding engine, with boiler, engine room and boiler house was making excellent progress. This, and the headgear, and rock breaking installations, would be completed within three months. The calciner, with its extensive system of chambers, was finished, except for closing the doorways, and the driving motor due for delivery. The tin yard, situated below the calciner, for which the excavations had been almost completed, should be ready in time to deal with their first parcel of calcined concentrates. The whole stuff would fall out from the top of the buildings, and, there being no elevation, the operation would be entirely automatic.

The directors' report contained an interesting note on Allen's Shaft. This, measuring 19 feet 6 inches by 6 feet within, had been sunk 200 feet from surface, the footage for the last fortnight being 12 feet 6 inches per week. At the collar, 40 feet of concrete was built. The rock was an altered clay slate, its hardness being such that the St. Just District Council had purchased 100 cubic yards for macadamising the parish roads. The loading for the winding engine was complete, and the engine itself being erected. The walls of the engine house were nearly ready for the roof, whilst excavations were being made for a Lancashire boiler. The chimney was 40 feet above the foundations. The labour force of about 300 was distributed as follows: Allen's Shaft section, 54; Nineveh, 21; Wheal Cock, 10; Botallack adits, 9; Wheal Hazard, 6; and Carnyorth 6; one-half of the remainder being general labourers, whose numbers would be reduced as construction work neared completion.

Writing on September 30th to Francis Allen, William Thomas, the ex-manager, set out at length the reasons which had influenced him to undertake the unwatering of Wheal Cock and Nineveh in preference to the Botallack section, as the preliminary step to opening up the entire run of mines. After listing various practical considerations, he concluded by stressing the most important point in the whole undertaking, "viz., that it is certain the ultimate success of the property depends largely upon the speed with which the approaching junction of Wheal

Cock and the Crowns lodes is reached. The chief ore bodies undoubtedly occur in the vicinity of the junction of the Killas and Granite which dips seawards in Botallack as in Levant. Having regard to the results already obtained in this direction at Levant, this is the *main point* to bear in mind, in any scheme for draining the workings in the Botallack Mines."

His letter was apparently written in an attempt to persuade the directors to revert to this scheme; but they decided upon a contrary mode of development. Another report had been submitted to them, stating opinion that the policy of unwatering Botallack section alone was preferable to draining Wheal Cock and Nineveh alone, as the capital expenditure would probably be less; there were better prospects of obtaining ore for the mill at an early date; and that in order to continue the sinking of Allen's Shaft, Botallack old workings must first be cleared of water.

The directors, in their annual report dated August 13th 1909, stated that the results so far achieved, consequent on their decision to unwater Botallack old workings, had proved this policy to be a sound one. The unwatering had proceeded steadily, though frequent chokages in the shaft occasioned delay. Sufficient material, of a payable grade, all coming from above adit level, had been extracted to supplement that coming from the dumps. Their future plan was to open up new ground, which would be effected by resuming the sinking of Allen's Shaft.

By May 22nd 1908, Allen's Shaft had been sunk 295 feet from surface, at which depth cross-cuts were started both N. and S. The sinking of the shaft was continued, and on September 2nd, at a depth of 360 feet, they cut a stream of water which quickly filled the shaft to within 15 feet of adit level. Meantime, development of a lode intersected at adit level continued, and the E. drive 84 feet distant from the main cross-cut proved this vein to be entering the granite, while a few feet further drivage encountered old workings which extended above and below the level. This proved that the water struck in Allen's Shaft had come from these old workings which were not shown on the mine plan, and it was therefore realised that nothing further could be done unless Botallack mine was unwatered. 1,255 feet of development had been carried out in this section, including the clearance of Cliffield adit, the ore raised amounting to 2,010 tons 8 cwt., all of payable quality.

After the flooding of Allen's Shaft it was decided to re-open Botallack Engine Shaft to drain this section, and to confine working to this part of the property. This work was commenced around September 15th, and by December 7th they had cleared and re timbered the shaft from surface to adit, a depth of 300 feet. On this date they started hoisting ore which had been mined from the old stopes during October and November. By the 19th, 411 tons of ore raised had assayed at 28 lbs.

of black tin per ton. The shaft was then equipped with a skipway, a new headgear with ore bin erected, and a self-dumping skip installed. A transmission line was taken from the power house to the new head gear, pump winch erected, shaft cable laid and cable drum erected in the station already prepared at adit level by April 13th, and on the 15th unwatering operations commenced. Meantime, the old adit level was re-opened, and 1,500 feet of levels cleared and repaired. The "clearings" from these and old stopes above, together with small lots of ore mined from these and old stopes above, together with small lots of ore mined from December 7th 1908, to June 26th 1909, produced 6,784 tons of ore, assaying at an average of 18 lbs. of tin per ton, or a total tin content of almost 56 tons.

To assist drainage, Durloe adit was cleared, 1,673 feet having been done by July 20th, with a further 200 feet to go to reach the source of the water. On July 6th, in spite of a completely choked shaft, they had unwatered the mine to the 80 fathom level, which was being cleared, together with the 60 E. of Botallack Shaft.

A trial run of the mill and concentrating plant had taken place on June 15th, but the running of the plant had been for a time intermittent owing to water shortage. By July 19th they began dressing the first parcel of tin in the tin yard. A settling plant with return water pump was also built with catchment pits for slimes, and a systematic water service laid out.

Tonnage milled from August 1st 1908, to July 31st 1909, had been:

Botallack Dumps	15,900 t. 11 cwt.	
Nineveh	276 t. 15 cwt.	
Total		16,177 t. 6 cwt.
Nineveh Mine Ore	1,772 t. 5 cwt.	
Allen's	2,732 t. 16 cwt.	
Botallack	7,600 t. 8 cwt.	
Total		12,105 t 9 cwt.
		28,282 t. 15 cwt.

Tin produced: Dumps, 34.5%. Mine ore, 65.5%.

The balance sheet to March 1909, showed that of the £150,000 authorised capital (in £1 shares), 100,000 shares had been issued. Purchase of properties had accounted for £40,750; development expenditure, £16,653 17s. 11d.; further expenditure on shafts, adits, &c., £9,222; buildings, £15,131 19s. 2d.; and fixed plant and machinery, £25,682 5s. 5d. The loss for nine months to date had been £3,945 12s. 7d.

By August, the heavy development costs being incurred made a financial reorganisation of the mine necessary. The Chairman accordingly announced the issue of £10,000 income bonds of £10 each on which a bonus of £5 would be payable in yearly instalments. The Cornish Consolidated Co. had advanced £20,000 to the mine and was in no hurry for repayment. The intention was to convert the Income Bonds into 5% First Mortgage Debentures, which would form part of £50,000 debentures to be issued when required. On the advice of the general manager and Messrs. Bainbridge, Seymour & Co. (consulting engineers) the additional capital would be used to sink Allen's Central Shaft another 40 fathoms, bringing them into practically virgin ground which it was hoped would keep their battery fully employed on mine ore.[3] In the event, the reconstruction carried out proved to be far more drastic than was forecast in this statement, and resulted in Botallack Mines, Ltd., going into liquidation, its assets being taken over by a new Company called Botallack, Limited.

An extraordinary general meeting of Botallack shareholders was held on February 18th 1910, under the chairmanship of Francis Allen. It was resolved that 29,790 shares of £1 each numbered 100,001 to 129,790, part of the unissued capital, should be divided into 119,160 "A" shares of 6s. each. Holders of these "A" shares were to be entitled, in proportion to the number of shares held by them respectively, to 5% of the money value of the tin sold each year, and to half of the yearly profits, the other half to provide dividends on the ordinary shares. W. R. Thomas having resigned as manager, Messrs. Bainbridge, Seymour & Co. were placed in temporary management. A report of this meeting in the *Mining Magazine*, mentioned that the site of Allen's Shaft had been chosen "by the plans at the Falmouth office, and approved by Mr. Skewes, Lord Falmouth's mineral agent. Any blame attached to the site choice must be attributed to those who were responsible for keeping an accurate plan of the early workings. The keeping down of the water in Cock section did not reduce the water in the old workings, and it became necessary to abandon pumping here, and transfer it to Botallack section, whereby the water in the old workings was lowered and gave freedom to go on sinking the new shaft. Unexpected snags occurred in unwatering Botallack, which was reported to be clear down to 90 fathoms, but was choked by debris which had been thrown in. Warning had been given of a dam supposed to exist at the 80 fathom level, and all levels had to be cleared to ensure that there were no chokages which may have been holding back a dangerous amount of water. The dam at the 80 was found to be only of brick 2 feet thick, and to be holding back 20 fathoms of water. At considerable risk Capt. Stratton went down and blew out the dam. Three trips were required; he had previously carried out a similar and less hazardous operation at Nineveh."

The water in Botallack now stood between 90 and 100 fathoms which would be kept 30 feet below the bottom of the new shaft. Allen's Shaft was sinking at 10 feet per week, its present depth being 510 feet below the shaft collar. Messrs. Bainbridge, Seymour & Co. advised sinking another 700 feet, which would bring the shaft below the level of the old workings. The old workings broken into at the 50 continued down and were intersected by cross-cutting at the 70. They were full of deads which yielded 18-22 lbs. per ton when milled. They were no longer crushing dump ore and no further expenditure on plant was envisaged; the money asked for was solely for sinking the new shift.

The prospectus of Botallack, Limited, showed that its capital was to consist of 100,000 shares of £1 each. The directors were Francis Allen, Lieut. Gen. Sir Reginald Pole Carew and Harry J. Meyerstein; manager, A. B. Climas; with offices at St. Just. The document stated that Allen's Shaft had been sunk to 138 fathoms and equipped to a depth of 130 fathoms. During the clearing up operations above adit over 250 tons of black tin had already been recovered from the mine debris, and seven tons were being regularly produced per month. This should increase as Allen's Shaft continued to be sunk at the rate of 7 fathoms per month. A new lode in virgin ground was met with in the 70 fathom level in Allen's Shaft, which gave excellent assay values for tin. So far as development work had progressed (110 feet) the average value over a stoping width of 2 feet 6 inches was 60 lb. of tin per ton. A cross-cut had been started at the 90 fathom level to block out this piece of ground.

Botallack section had been unwatered to 149 fathoms and the Crowns to 65 fathoms. It was intended to connect Allen's, Botallack and the Crowns at the 150 level in Allen's Shaft, and centre all the pumping there. This work should be completed by the end of February. A search had been made for pitchblende, which proved successful. A French engineer, who had made a special study of radium ores, visited the property, and thoroughly sampled the mine. These samples were assayed at Madame Curie's laboratory in Paris, and the engineer had reported that they were the richest samples he had come across. The first $1^1/_2$ tons of crude ore sent to Paris realised £150.

Over £70,000 had been spent on the property by the existing company. Messrs. Edmundson's Electricity Corporation were to supply the mine with electric power from their Hayle station, which would reduce operating expenses and save a substantial outlay for further power plant as the mine developed. It was estimated that the working costs would be 18s. 6d. per ton when 40 head of stamps were at work (at present they had 20, with a further 20 delivered). On this basis, and calculating 42,000 tons per annum yielding 40 lbs. per ton, or 750 tons of black tin at £90 (the current price being £110 per ton) worth £67,500, a profit could be anticipated amounting to 35 per cent to those applying for shares offered at 5s. paid. When a further 20 head of stamps had been erected, a dividend of over 50 per cent could be anticipated.

In the following year (1912) the *Mining Magazine* remarked that Botallack had "given much trouble to the people associated with it at various times and in different capacities during the last six years". Since the last reorganisation, in March 1911, 95,984 of the 100,000 £1 shares had been issued, and debentures worth £23,250 subscribed. During that time (to June 30) 28,431 tons of ore were stamped, 10,199 coming from the mine and 18,232 from the dumps. The yield of concentrate was 142 tons, or about 11 lbs. of black tin per ton—a miserably low recovery rate, and far below what had been anticipated. It had been decided to erect the additional 20 head of stamps that had been on the mine for some time, bringing the battery to 30 head. The current mining cost was £14,765, whilst in addition £23,004 had been spent on capital development.

In May 1913, the same source reported: "It is unfortunate that the grade of ore milled shows no improvement. Indeed, the average recovery for the 16 weeks ended April 5th is slightly less than the 11 lb. average shown in the last annual report. The tonnage handled last month was 2,350, the sales amounting to 12 tons 2 cwt., which produced £1,620." However, during the four weeks ending September 20th, the recovery rose to 20 lb. per ton, a decided increase on previous monthly figures. For the nine months ending September 29th, 110 tons of black tin were sold at the ticketing for £13,877. During the same period in 1912 the figures were 80 tons and £10,203. To provide additional crushing machinery, an issue of £10,000 6 per cent debentures had been arranged. These debentures would rank as a first charge on the property and assets of the company, over-riding the existing debentures.

The annual report issued in December for the year ending June 30th 1913, did not make cheerful reading. During this period, Allen's Shaft was sunk 110 feet, at an average cost of £18 8s. per foot, the depth from surface being 1,477 feet. A large amount of development work had been carried out on the No. 2 lode at the 7th, 8th, 9th and 10th levels, and whilst results in the first two had been fairly satisfactory, the lode in the 9th and 10th levels had been narrow in width and poor in quality, and all work in the bottom had been suspended pending developments in the levels above. The developments on Narrow lode, on which great hopes had been placed in view of past results, had also been disappointing. The lode was attacked at the 6th, 7th and 8th levels, but though averaging 20 feet in width, it showed no ore of value, and gave no indication of improvement. The management thought this disappearance of ore resulted from the change in the country rock from killas to granite. "In this district, no ore of any consequence has been found in the granite, as witness the result of development at Levant." During the year, 11,980 tons from the mine and 13,208 from the dump were treated, for a yield of only 131 tons of black tin, or less than 12 lb. per ton. This sold for £17,572, while the cost was £18,377. In addition, London expenses absorbed £1,903, and £1,208 was due on debenture interest. During the year, the extraction problem had been given much study, and efforts made to increase the percentage of recovery. Trials were made with the volatilisation process, but without satisfactory results. Since then, additional slime plant had been erected. Ten of the other twenty stamps that had been on the mine since 1907 had been put to work since the end of the year under review, making 30 in all, with the object of reducing the cost per ton.

The chairman's speech was cast in very gloomy terms: "In March 1912, the Company required further money to complete the development of the property, and accordingly have issued £25,550 debentures realising £23,000. This expenditure has enabled us to complete the shaft sinking for the present, and to open up the No. 2 lode down to some 300 feet below the bottom of the old working, and some 800 feet below on the Narrow lode. If a reasonable proportion of the Narrow lode had proved payable this would have been amply sufficient to run 40 stamps. It is a very wide lode, but it has been found quite barren, though there may be some chance of finding ore to the W. of the Hazard Shaft . . . more development must be done to prepare enough ground to keep the mill going, and entails a heavy charge for development redemption, probably amounting to about 5s. per ton."

Taking a stoping width of 2½ feet, there had been developed to date some 22,000 to 30,000 tons of ore, averaging about 30 lbs. of black tin per ton, but the very patchy nature of the ground made it doubtful whether these figures would actually be realised. The last two months' returns, being much worse than expected, had brought matters to a head sooner than expected. "There is no doubt that you would be within your right if you decide to foreclose, but it is not a course I would recommend, as unless you decide to abandon the mine immediately with the 20-30,000 tons of developed ore, you must raise further money, which, in any case, would be a prior charge, and if work is stopped now for want of money, a heavy loss . . . will be incurred. The monthly cost of pumping is now over £200, and if the mine shut down it could not be done for that."

The development policy which the directors had chosen to follow at the commencement of operations was now bearing its bitter fruit of failure; and, short of making a completely new start, working the undersea portion as the prime objective, there could be no hope of retrieving the situation. But there could be no question of making a new start. Years of disappointment had taken the heart out of the investors, whilst the prevailing world situation was against any ventures of that kind. Rodda's Almanack tersely records that Botallack Mine closed on March 14th 1914, just five months before the outbreak of the first World War.

1 A detailed report of the proceedings will be found in E. W. Meyerstein's *A Key to Cornish Mining* (1907).
2 Wheal Owles stopped in 1893, after being flooded when workmen broke into the abandoned workings of Wheal Drea. At that time it was still making profits, with tin at £50 a ton.
3 Thomas, *A Souvenir, West of England Conference*, 1909. This very rare booklet contains accounts of Dolcoath, South Crofty and Botallack mines.

INDEX